Kern County Library

1. Books may be kept until last due date on card in this pocket.

2. A fine will be charged on each book which is not returned by date due.

3. All injuries to books beyond reasonable wear and all losses shall be made good to the satisfaction of the librarian.

4. Each borrower is held responsible for all books borrowed by him and for all fines accruing on them.

DEMCO

Poems of Walt Whitman: LEAVES OF GRASS

POEMS OF WALT WHITMAN

LEAVES
OF GRASS

Selected by Lawrence Clark Powell

Woodcuts by John Ross
and Clare Romano Ross

Thomas Y. Crowell Company · New York

Contents

Walt Whitman

These poems chosen from Whitman's *Leaves of Grass* are both meat for the young to grow on and medicine to heal the older who have been hurt by life. This is not someone else's literary theory; it is my own experience. I have had *Leaves of Grass* as part of my life since childhood. There has always been a handy copy I could reach for and read in, although the first one I ever saw, the one belonging to my mother and father, puzzled me by its title: did grass have leaves? I used to stare at the back of the book, from where I lay taking a forced nap in the family library, and wonder what it was all about. I was a city boy, and the only grass I knew as a child was our carefully mown front lawn.

When I went to high school Whitman was *not* required reading, and in college the professor who taught American literature said Longfellow was our greatest American poet. I didn't believe him. In France, however, where I did postgraduate study, I found Walt Whitman to be one of their literary gods. Years later, in Japan, I discussed *Leaves of Grass* with students in Kyoto. Through all these long years I have gone on reading Whitman, finding him changing as I changed, yet always at my side, in my need a good guide.

I regard *Leaves of Grass* as the greatest single book American literature has yet produced. But it needs weeding and pruning for those who are reading it for the first time. Whitman published it in 1855 when he was thirty-five; it was his one and only book of poetry. For nearly forty years he kept adding to and rearranging its contents, until by the time he died in 1892, old and bearded and almost respectable, what had been a thin book of pure muscle had grown thick and fat.

So I have reduced it in weight, taking some liberties with the author's original arrangement, retaining what I have found through my own lifetime of reading to be the most intense and powerful of the poems. I have included only excerpts from several of the longer ones. The sectional headings are my own.

I said Whitman had become almost respectable by the time he died. This is still true, going on a century after his death; his poetry still has the power to shock. His poems about men and women and love, written in the prime of his life, are strong and outspoken and true.

But Whitman didn't write to shock people. He wrote because he was in love with life. In his early thirties he was full of the juice of joy. He loved his country and its natural beauty from sea to shining sea; he loved men and women, each and every part of them, from bare head to naked feet.

3

No one in America had ever written poetry of such frankness. *Leaves of Grass* burst like a bombshell. Longfellow ignored it. Whittier threw his copy in the fire. Most critics and readers dove into their shelters for protection. One didn't. The greatest literary figure of his time, the New Englander Ralph Waldo Emerson, took the full impact of the book, braced himself, and wrote to Whitman:

"I find it the most extraordinary piece of wit and wisdom that America has yet contributed. I am very happy in reading it, as great power makes us happy. I have great joy in it. I find incomparable things, said incomparably well. I greet you at the beginning of a great career."

It was a great career—and a stormy one. *Leaves of Grass* was censored and suppressed, and Whitman had trouble holding a job because he was regarded by the authorities as the author of an unhealthy book.

On the contrary, *Leaves of Grass* is one of the healthiest books ever written. It is a shout of joy for life, a hymn of praise for death. It is also a love poem to America the beautiful, to earth, sea, and sky, as well as to the beauty and dignity of natural man. *Leaves of Grass* has never been out of print since its birth in 1855; it has been translated into all the languages of the world. It is part of our American heritage and legacy to mankind.

"Who touches this book," Whitman wrote of *Leaves of Grass*, "touches a man." *A* man, yes, not *the* man Whitman. *Leaves of Grass* is not to be read as autobiography. Whitman was not an emotional adventurer; his is the old story of the artist's fulfillment in literature rather than in life. *Leaves of Grass* is a work of the creative imagination, not a personal confession. How it came to be written by this particular man remains a mystery, the causes being complex and subtle and impossible to isolate in precise detail.

This is the way it always is with great literature. The who, why, when, and where of the creative act can never be predicted; after it happens, it can never be understood.

The outward facts of Whitman's life are known. He was born, the second of nine children, on May 31, 1819, on a farm near Huntington, Long Island. The family was under the influence of Elias Hicks, the well-known Quaker preacher. When Walt was four they moved to Brooklyn. He became a printer, newspaperman, and schoolteacher in Brooklyn and on Long Island; he was also indolent, a loafer, a great reader, and a lover of music. He made one trip of a few months to work on a newspaper in New Orleans. Not until he was an old man did he travel beyond the Mississippi, and then only a quick trip as far as Denver. During the Civil War he was a volunteer nurse in the hospitals of Virginia; afterward he held a clerkship in Washington. The last twenty years of his life he was a semi-invalid from a stroke, living in New Jersey.

Except for his part in the Civil War, his was not an outwardly eventful life. Whitman's great activity was inward, was of the mind and the emotions, of the intellect and the imagination. The greatest single force that caused *Leaves of Grass* to erupt in him was the influence of Ralph Waldo Emerson. Of his life during the years before *Leaves* appeared in 1855, Whitman wrote, "I was simmering, simmering, simmering; Emerson brought me to a boil."

That is why Whitman sent his book to Emerson as an act of thanksgiving, from pupil to master. It was his answer to the essays Emerson had written, calling for a native American literature that would strike off the shackles of European tradition and prophesying the flowering of democratic American individualism.

Leaves of Grass went beyond Emerson's call in its unrhymed formlessness and its glorification of the human body. Though shaken by it, Emerson did not repudiate it. If he proved unsuccessful in persuading Whitman to leave some of the more outspoken poems out of later editions, Emerson never withdrew his friendship for the Quaker poet. Here is what he wrote to the Englishman Carlyle: "One book, last summer, came out in New York, a nondescript monster which yet had terrible eyes and buffalo strength, and was indisputably American. It is called *Leaves of Grass*—was written and printed by a journeyman printer in Brooklyn, named Walter Whitman."

"Terrible eyes and buffalo strength"—no one has ever described Whitman's genius with more truth and power and beauty.

Briefly, the forces which coalesced in Whitman to create his book were his love of mankind, nature, the city, and the whole wide country; his response to Emerson's call; his reaction to the Civil War, which threatened to destroy America; his reverence for Lincoln; and, finally, his reconciliation with death, the end of life. "Reconciliation, word over all, beautiful as the sky," he wrote, in one of those transcendent flashes which continually light up the book.

To the first edition of *Leaves of Grass,* which Whitman himself set in type, and which instead of his name on the title page bore his own picture as frontispiece, the poet wrote a preface which was omitted from later editions. This is a great pity, for it is the best thing ever written about the poems. Perhaps he dropped it because it too precisely revealed his debt to Emerson; in fact it reads like an Emerson essay. Although, as I have noted, Whitman acknowledged the Concord sage as his teacher, he did not want to dwell on the acknowledgment.

This preface is Whitman's manifesto to then and now. Here is one of the most moving passages from it, as applicable now as it was then, his charge to his fellow men, to them and to us, to you and to me, of which his poems are a glorious expansion.

"This is what you shall do: love the earth and sun and the animals, despise riches, give alms to everyone that asks, stand up for the stupid and crazy, devote your income and labor to others, hate tyrants, argue not concerning God, have patience and indulgence toward the people, take off your hat to nothing known or unknown or to any man or number of men, go freely with powerful uneducated persons and with the young and with the mothers of families, read these leaves in the open air every season of every year of your life, re-examine all you have been told at school or church or in any book, dismiss whatever insults your own soul, and your very flesh shall be a great poem and have the richest fluency not only in its words but in the silent lines of its lips and face and between the lashes of your eyes and in every motion and joint of your body."

LAWRENCE CLARK POWELL

AMERICA

THE BEAUTIFUL

I Hear America Singing

I hear America singing, the varied carols I hear,
Those of mechanics, each one singing his as it should be
      blithe and strong,
The carpenter singing his as he measures his plank or beam,
The mason singing his as he makes ready for work, or leaves
      off work,
The boatman singing what belongs to him in his boat, the deck-
      hand singing on the steamboat deck,
The shoemaker singing as he sits on his bench, the hatter sing-
      ing as he stands,
The wood-cutter's song, the ploughboy's on his way in the
      morning, or at noon intermission or at sundown,
The delicious singing of the mother, or of the young wife at
      work, or of the girl sewing or washing,
Each singing what belongs to him or her and to none else,
The day what belongs to the day—at night the party of young
      fellows, robust, friendly,
Singing with open mouths their strong melodious songs.

Mediums

They shall arise in the States,
They shall report Nature, laws, physiology, and happiness,
They shall illustrate Democracy and the kosmos,
They shall be alimentive, amative, perceptive,
They shall be complete women and men, their pose brawny and
      supple, their drink water, their blood clean and clear,
They shall fully enjoy materialism and the sight of products,
      they shall enjoy the sight of the beef, lumber, bread-
      stuffs, of Chicago the great city,
They shall train themselves to go in public to become orators
      and oratresses,
Strong and sweet shall their tongues be, poems and materials
      of poems shall come from their lives, they shall be mak-
      ers and finders,
Of them and of their works shall emerge divine conveyers, to
      convey gospels,
Characters, events, retrospections, shall be convey'd in gospels,
      trees, animals, waters, shall be convey'd,
Death, the future, the invisible faith, shall all be convey'd.

Sparkles from the Wheel

Where the city's ceaseless crowd moves on the livelong day,
Withdrawn I join a group of children watching, I pause aside
    with them.

By the curb toward the edge of the flagging,
A knife-grinder works at his wheel sharpening a great knife,
Bending over he carefully holds it to the stone, by foot and
    knee,
With measur'd tread he turns rapidly, as he presses with light
    but firm hand,
Forth issue then in copious golden jets,
Sparkles from the wheel.

The scene and all its belongings, how they seize and affect me,
The sad sharp-chinn'd old man with worn clothes and broad
    shoulder-band of leather,
Myself effusing and fluid, a phantom curiously floating, now
    here absorb'd and arrested,
The group, (an unminded point set in a vast surrounding,)
The attentive, quiet children, the loud, proud, restive base of
    the streets,
The low hoarse purr of the whirling stone, the light-press'd
    blade,
Diffusing, dropping, sideways-darting, in tiny showers of gold,
Sparkles from the wheel.

Mannahatta

I was asking for something specific and perfect for my city,
Whereupon lo! upsprang the aboriginal name.

Now I see what there is in a name, a word, liquid, sane, un-
       ruly, musical, self-sufficient,
I see that the word of my city is that word from of old,
Because I see that word nested in nests of water-bays, superb,
Rich, hemm'd thick all around with sailships and steamships,
       an island sixteen miles long, solid-founded.
Numberless crowded streets, high growth of iron, slender,
       strong, light, splendidly uprising toward clear skies,
Tides swift and ample, well-loved by me, toward sundown,
The flowing sea-currents, the little islands, larger adjoining is-
       lands, the heights, the villas,
The countless masts, the white shore-steamers, the lighters, the
       ferry-boats, the black sea-steamers well-model'd,
The down-town streets, the jobbers' houses of business, the
       houses of business of the ship-merchants and money-
       brokers, the river-streets,
Immigrants arriving, fifteen or twenty thousand in a week,
The carts hauling goods, the manly race of drivers of horses,
       the brown-faced sailors,
The summer air, the bright sun shining, and the sailing clouds
       aloft,
The winter snows, the sleigh-bells, the broken ice in the river,
       passing along up or down with the flood-tide or ebb-
       tide,
The mechanics of the city, the masters, well-form'd, beautiful-
       faced, looking you straight in the eyes,
Trottoirs throng'd, vehicles, Broadway, the women, the shops
       and shows,
A million people—manners free and superb—open voices—
       hospitality—the most courageous and friendly young
       men,
City of hurried and sparkling waters! city of spires and masts!
City nested in bays! my city!

By Broad Potomac's Shore

By broad Potomac's shore, again old tongue,
(Still uttering, still ejaculating, canst never cease this babble?)
Again old heart so gay, again to you, your sense, the full flush
     spring returning,
Again the freshness and the odors, again Virginia's summer
     sky, pellucid blue and silver,
Again the forenoon purple of the hills,
Again the deathless grass, so noiseless soft and green,
Again the blood-red roses blooming.

Perfume this book of mine O blood-red roses!
Lave subtly with your waters every line Potomac!
Give me of you O spring, before I close, to put between its
     pages!
O forenoon purple of the hills, before I close, of you!
O deathless grass, of you!

Pioneers! O Pioneers!

Come my tan-faced children,
Follow well in order, get your weapons ready,
Have you your pistols? have you your sharp-edged axes?
        Pioneers! O pioneers!

For we cannot tarry here,
We must march my darlings, we must bear the brunt of danger,
We the youthful sinewy races, all the rest on us depend,
        Pioneers! O pioneers!

O you youths, Western youths,
So impatient, full of action, full of manly pride and friendship,
Plain I see you Western youths, see you tramping with the fore-
        most,
        Pioneers! O pioneers!

Have the elder races halted?
Do they droop and end their lesson, wearied over there beyond
        the seas
We take up the task eternal, and the burden and the lesson,
        Pioneers! O pioneers!

All the past we leave behind,
We debouch upon a newer mightier world, varied world,
Fresh and strong the world we seize, world of labor and the
        march,
        Pioneers! O pioneers!

We detachments steady throwing,
Down the edges, through the passes, up the mountains steep,
Conquering, holding, daring, venturing as we go the unknown
        ways,
        Pioneers! O pioneers!

We primeval forests felling,
We the rivers stemming, vexing we and piercing deep the
    mines within,
We the surface broad surveying, we the virgin soil upheaving,
        Pioneers! O pioneers!

Colorado men are we,
From the peaks gigantic, from the great sierras and the high
    plateaus,
From the mine and from the gully, from the hunting trail we
    come,
        Pioneers! O pioneers!

From Nebraska, from Arkansas,
Central inland race are we, from Missouri, with the continental
    blood intervein'd,
All the hands of comrades clasping, all the Southern, all the
    Northern,
        Pioneers! O pioneers!

O resistless restless race!
O beloved race in all! O my breast aches with tender love for
    all!
O I mourn and yet exult, I am rapt with love for all,
        Pioneers! O pioneers!

Raise the mighty mother mistress,
Waving high the delicate mistress, over all the starry mistress,
    (bend your heads all,)
Raise the fang'd and warlike mistress, stern, impassive, weap-
    on'd mistress,
        Pioneers! O pioneers!

See my children, resolute children,
By those swarms upon our rear we must never yield or falter,
Ages back in ghostly millions frowning there behind us urging,
      Pioneers! O pioneers!

On and on the compact ranks,
With accessions ever waiting, with the places of the dead
    quickly fill'd,
Through the battle, through defeat, moving yet and never stop-
    ping,
      Pioneers! O pioneers!

O to die advancing on!
Are there some of us to droop and die? has the hour come?
Then upon the march we fittest die, soon and sure the gap is
    fill'd,
      Pioneers! O pioneers!

All the pulses of the world,
Falling in they beat for us, with the Western movement beat,
Holding single or together, steady moving to the front, all for
    us,
      Pioneers! O pioneers!

Life's involv'd and varied pageants,
All the forms and shows, all the workmen at their work,
All the seamen and the landsmen, all the masters with their
    slaves,
      Pioneers! O pioneers!

All the hapless silent lovers,
All the prisoners in the prisons, all the righteous and the
    wicked,
All the joyous, all the sorrowing, all the living, all the dying,
      Pioneers! O pioneers!

I too with my soul and body,
We, a curious trio, picking, wandering on our way,
Through these shores amid the shadows, with the apparitions
  pressing,
  Pioneers! O pioneers!

Lo, the darting bowling orb!
Lo, the brother orbs around, all the clustering suns and planets,
All the dazzling days, all the mystic nights with dreams,
  Pioneers! O pioneers!

These are of us, they are with us,
All for primal needed work, while the followers there in em-
  bryo wait behind,
We to-day's procession heading, we the route for travel clear-
  ing,
  Pioneers! O pioneers!

O you daughters of the West!
O you young and elder daughters! O you mothers and you
  wives!
Never must you be divided, in our ranks you move united,
  Pioneers! O pioneers!

Minstrels latent on the prairies!
(Shrouded bards of other lands, you may rest, you have done
  your work,)
Soon I hear you coming warbling, soon you rise and tramp
  amid us,
  Pioneers! O pioneers!

Not for delectations sweet,
Not the cushion and the slipper, not the peaceful and the studi-
  ous,
Not the riches safe and palling, not for us the tame enjoyment,
  Pioneers! O pioneers!

Do the feasters gluttonous feast?
Do the corpulent sleepers sleep? have they lock'd and bolted
doors?
Still be ours the diet hard, and the blanket on the ground,
Pioneers! O pioneers!

Has the night descended?
Was the road of late so toilsome? did we stop discouraged nod-
ding on our way?
Yet a passing hour I yield you in your tracks to pause oblivi-
ous,
Pioneers! O pioneers!

Till with sound of trumpet,
Far, far off the daybreak call—hark! how loud and clear I hear
it wind,
Swift! to the head of the army!—swift! spring to your places,
Pioneers! O pioneers!

The Commonplace

The commonplace I sing;
How cheap is health! how cheap nobility!
Abstinence, no falsehood, no gluttony, lust;
The open air I sing, freedom, toleration,
(Take here the mainest lesson—less from books—less from the
schools,)
The common day and night—the common earth and waters,
Your farm—your work, trade, occupation,
The democratic wisdom underneath, like solid ground for all.

19

I Saw in Louisiana a Live-Oak Growing

I saw in Louisiana a live-oak growing,
All alone stood it and the moss hung down from the branches,
Without any companion it grew there uttering joyous leaves of
      dark green,
And its look, rude, unbending, lusty, made me think of myself,
But I wonder'd how it could utter joyous leaves standing alone
      there without its friend near, for I knew I could not,
And I broke off a twig with a certain number of leaves upon it,
      and twined around it a little moss,
And brought it away, and I have placed it in sight in my room,
It is not needed to remind me as of my own dear friends,
(For I believe lately I think of little else than of them,)
Yet it remains to me a curious token, it makes me think of
      manly love;
For all that, and though the live-oak glistens there in Louisiana
      solitary in a wide flat space,
Uttering joyous leaves all its life without a friend a lover near,
I know very well I could not.

Night on the Prairies

Night on the prairies,
The supper is over, the fire on the ground burns low,
The wearied emigrants sleep, wrapt in their blankets;
I walk by myself—I stand and look at the stars, which I think
   now I never realized before.

Now I absorb immortality and peace,
I admire death and test propositions.
How plenteous! how spiritual! how resumé!
The same old man and soul—the same old aspirations, and
   the same content.

I was thinking the day most splendid till I saw what the not-day
   exhibited,
I was thinking this globe enough till there sprang out so noiseless around me myriads of other globes.

Now while the great thoughts of space and eternity fill me I
   will measure myself by them,
And now touch'd with the lives of other globes arrived as far
   along as those of the earth,
Or waiting to arrive, or pass'd on farther than those of the
   earth,
I henceforth no more ignore them than I ignore my own life,
Or the lives of the earth arrived as far as mine, or waiting to arrive.

O I see now that life cannot exhibit all to me, as the day cannot,
I see that I am to wait for what will be exhibited by death.

Song of the Broad-Axe

Weapon shapely, naked, wan,
Head from the mother's bowels drawn,
Wooded flesh and metal bone, limb only one and lip only one,
Gray-blue leaf by red-heat grown, helve produced from a little
    seed sown,
Resting the grass amid and upon,
To be lean'd and to lean on.

Strong shapes and attributes of strong shapes, masculine trades,
    sights and sounds,
Long varied train of an emblem, dabs of music,
Fingers of the organist skipping staccato over the keys of the
    great organ.

. . . .

4

Muscle and pluck forever!
What invigorates life invigorates death,
And the dead advance as much as the living advance,
And the future is no more uncertain than the present,
For the roughness of the earth and of man encloses as much as
    the delicatesse of the earth and of man,
And nothing endures but personal qualities.

What do you think endures?
Do you think a great city endures?
Or a teeming manufacturing state? or a prepared constitution?
    or the best-built steamships?
Or hotels of granite and iron? or any chef-d'œuvres of engi-
    neering, forts, armaments?
Away! these are not to be cherish'd for themselves,
They fill their hour, the dancers dance, the musicians play for
    them,
The show passes, all does well enough of course,
All does very well till one flash of defiance.

A great city is that which has the greatest men and women,
If it be a few ragged huts it is still the greatest city in the whole
     world.

.   .   .   .

9

(America! I do not vaunt my love for you,
I have what I have.)

The axe leaps!
The solid forest gives fluid utterances,
They tumble forth, they rise and form,
Hut, tent, landing, survey,
Flail, plough, pick, crowbar, spade,
Shingle, rail, prop, wainscot, jamb, lath, panel, gable,
Citadel, ceiling, saloon, academy, organ, exhibition-house, li-
     brary,
Cornice, trellis, pilaster, balcony, window, turret, porch,
Hoe, rake, pitchfork, pencil, wagon, staff, saw, jack-plane, mal-
     let, wedge, rounce,
Chair, tub, hoop, table, wicket, vane, sash, floor,
Work-box, chest, string'd instrument, boat, frame, and what
     not,
Capitols of States, and capitol of the nation of States,
Long stately rows in avenues, hospitals for orphans or for the
     poor or sick,
Manhattan steamboats and clippers taking the measure of all
     seas.

The shapes arise!
Shapes of the using of axes anyhow, and the users and all that
     neighbors them,
Cutters down of wood and haulers of it to the Penobscot or
     Kennebec,
Dwellers in cabins among the Californian mountains or by the
     little lakes, or on the Columbia,

Dwellers south on the banks of the Gila or Rio Grande,
friendly gatherings, the characters and fun,
Dwellers along the St. Lawrence, or north in Kanada, or down
by the Yellowstone, dwellers on coasts and off coasts,
Seal-fishers, whalers, arctic seamen breaking passages through
the ice.

The shapes arise!
Shapes of factories, arsenals, foundries, markets,
Shapes of the two-threaded tracks of railroads,
Shapes of the sleepers of bridges, vast frameworks, girders,
arches,
Shapes of the fleets of barges, tows, lake and canal craft, river
craft,
Ship-yards and dry-docks along the Eastern and Western seas,
and in many a bay and by-place,
The live-oak kelsons, the pine planks, the spars, the hackma-
tack-roots for knees,
The ships themselves on their ways, the tiers of scaffolds, the
workmen busy outside and inside,
The tools lying around, the great auger and little auger, the
adze, bolt, line, square, gouge, and bead-plane.
·   ·   ·   ·   ·   ·   ·   ·   ·   ·   ·   ·   ·   ·

11

Her shape arises,
She less guarded than ever, yet more guarded than ever,
The gross and soil'd she moves among do not make her gross
and soil'd,
She knows the thoughts as she passes, nothing is conceal'd from
her,
She is none the less considerate or friendly therefor,
She is the best belov'd, it is without exception, she has no rea-
son to fear and she does not fear,
Oaths, quarrels, hiccupp'd songs, smutty expressions are idle to
her as she passes,

She is silent, she is possess'd of herself, they do not offend her,
She receives them as the laws of Nature receive them, she is
strong,
She too is a law of Nature—there is no law stronger than she is.

.   .   .   .

12

The main shapes arise!
Shapes of Democracy total, result of centuries,
Shapes ever projecting other shapes,
Shapes of turbulent manly cities,
Shapes of the friends and home-givers of the whole earth,
Shapes bracing the earth and braced with the whole earth.

To a Locomotive in Winter

Thee for my recitative,
Thee in the driving storm even as now, the snow, the winter-
day declining,
Thee in thy panoply, thy measur'd dual throbbing and thy
beat convulsive,
The black cylindric body, golden brass and silvery steel,
Thy ponderous side-bars, parallel and connecting rods, gyrat-
ing, shuttling at thy sides,
Thy metrical, now swelling pant and roar, now tapering in the
distance,

Thy great protruding head-light fix'd in front,
Thy long, pale, floating vapor-pennants, tinged with delicate
      purple,
The dense and murky clouds out-belching from thy smoke-
      stack,
Thy knitted frame, thy springs and valves, the tremulous twin-
      kle of thy wheels,
Thy train of cars, behind, obedient, merrily following,
Through gale or calm, now swift, now slack, yet steadily career-
      ing;
Type of the modern—emblem of motion and power—pulse of
      the continent,
For once come serve the Muse and merge in verse, even as
      here I see thee,
With storm and buffeting gusts of wind and falling snow,
By day thy warning ringing bell to sound its notes,
By night thy silent signal lamps to swing.

Fierce-throated beauty!
Roll through my chant with all thy lawless music, thy swinging
      lamps at night,
Thy madly-whistled laughter, echoing, rumbling like an earth-
      quake, rousing all,
Law of thyself complete, thine own track firmly holding,
(No sweetness debonair of tearful harp or glib piano thine,)
Thy trills of shrieks by rock and hills return'd,
Launch'd o'er the prairies wide, across the lakes,
To the free skies unpent and glad and strong.

Faces

1

Sauntering the pavement or riding the country by-road, lo,
    such faces!
Faces of friendship, precision, caution, suavity, ideality,
The spiritual-prescient face, the always welcome common be-
    nevolent face,
The face of the singing of music, the grand faces of natural law-
    yers and judges broad at the back-top,
The faces of hunters and fishers bulged at the brows, the
    shaved blanch'd faces of orthodox citizens,
The pure, extravagant, yearning, questioning artist's face,
The ugly face of some beautiful soul, the handsome detested
    or despised face,
The sacred faces of infants, the illuminated face of the mother
    of many children,
The face of an amour, the face of veneration,
The face as of a dream, the face of an immobile rock,
The face withdrawn of its good and bad, a castrated face,
A wild hawk, his wings clipp'd by the clipper,
A stallion that yielded at last to the thongs and knife of the
    gelder.

Sauntering the pavement thus, or crossing the ceaseless ferry,
    faces and faces and faces,
I see them and complain not, and am content with all.

2

Do you suppose I could be content with all if I thought them
    their own finalé?

This now is too lamentable a face for a man,
Some abject louse asking leave to be, cringing for it,
Some milk-nosed maggot blessing what lets it wrig to its hole.   **27**

This face is a dog's snout sniffing for garbage,

Snakes nest in that mouth, I hear the sibilant threat.

This face is a haze more chill than the arctic sea,
Its sleepy and wobbling icebergs crunch as they go.

This is a face of bitter herbs, this an emetic, they need no label,
And more of the drug-shelf, laudanum, caoutchouc, or hog's-
lard.

This face is an epilepsy, its wordless tongue gives out the unearthly cry,
Its veins down the neck distend, its eyes roll till they show nothing but their whites,
Its teeth grit, the palms of the hands are cut by the turn'd-in
nails,
The man falls struggling and foaming to the ground, while he
speculates well.

This face is bitten by vermin and worms,
And this is some murderer's knife with a half-pull'd scabbard.

This face owes to the sexton his dismalest fee,
An unceasing death-bell tolls there.

3

Features of my equals would you trick me with your creas'd
and cadaverous march?
Well, you cannot trick me.

I see your rounded never-erased flow,
I see 'neath the rims of your haggard and mean disguises.

Splay and twist as you like, poke with the tangling fores of
fishes or rats,
You'll be unmuzzled, you certainly will.

I saw the face of the most smear'd and slobbering idiot they
had at the asylum,

And I knew for my consolation what they knew not,
I knew of the agents that emptied and broke my brother,
The same wait to clear the rubbish from the fallen tenement,
And I shall look again in a score or two of ages,
And I shall meet the real landlord perfect and unharm'd, every
    inch as good as myself.

4

The Lord advances, and yet advances,
Always the shadow in front, always the reach'd hand bringing
    up the laggards.

Out of this face emerge banners and horses—O superb! I see
    what is coming,
I see the high pioneer-caps, see staves of runners clearing the
    way,
I hear victorious drums.

This face is a life-boat,
This is the face commanding and bearded, it asks no odds of
    the rest,
This face is flavor'd fruit ready for eating,
This face of a healthy honest boy is the programme of all good.

These faces bear testimony slumbering or awake,
They show their descent from the Master himself.

Of the word I have spoken I except not one—red, white, black,
    are all deific,
In each house is the ovum, it comes forth after a thousand years.

Spots or cracks at the windows do not disturb me,
Tall and sufficient stand behind and make signs to me,
I read the promise and patiently wait.

This is a full-grown lily's face,
She speaks to the limber-hipp'd man near the garden pickets,

Come here she blushingly cries, *Come nigh to me limber-*
hipp'd man,
Stand at my side till I lean as high as I can upon you,
Fill me with albescent honey, bend down to me,
Rub to me with your chafing beard, rub to my breast and shoul-
ders.

5

The old face of the mother of many children,
Whist! I am fully content.

Lull'd and late is the smoke of the First-day morning,
It hangs low over the rows of trees by the fences,
It hangs thin by the sassafras and wild-cherry and cat-brier un-
der them.

I saw the rich ladies in full dress at the soiree,
I heard what the singers were singing so long,
Heard who sprang in crimson youth from the white froth and
the water-blue.

Behold a woman!
She looks out from her quaker cap, her face is clearer and
more beautiful than the sky.

She sits in an armchair under the shaded porch of the farm-
house,
The sun just shines on her old white head.

Her ample gown is of cream-hued linen,
Her grandsons raised the flax, and her grand-daughters spin it
with the distaff and the wheel.

The melodious character of the earth,
The finish beyond which philosophy cannot go and does not
wish to go,
The justified mother of men.

Crossing Brooklyn Ferry

1

Flood-tide below me! I see you face to face!
Clouds of the west—sun there half an hour high—I see you
also face to face.

Crowds of men and women attired in the usual costumes, how
curious you are to me!
On the ferry-boats the hundreds and hundreds that cross, returning home, are more curious to me than you suppose,
And you that shall cross from shore to shore years hence are
more to me, and more in my meditations, than you
might suppose.

2

The impalpable sustenance of me from all things at all hours of
the day,
The simple, compact, well-join'd scheme, myself disintegrated,
every one disintegrated yet part of the scheme,
The similitudes of the past and those of the future,
The glories strung like beads on my smallest sights and hear-
ings, on the walk in the street and the passage over the
river,
The current rushing so swiftly and swimming with me far away,
The others that are to follow me, the ties between me and them,
The certainty of others, the life, love, sight, hearing of others.

Others will enter the gates of the ferry and cross from shore to
shore,
Others will watch the run of the flood-tide,
Others will see the shipping of Manhattan north and west, and
the heights of Brooklyn to the south and east,
Others will see the islands large and small;

31

Fifty years hence, others will see them as they cross, the sun
half an hour high,
A hundred years hence, or ever so many hundred years hence,
others will see them,
Will enjoy the sunset, the pouring-in of the flood-tide, the fall-
ing-back to the sea of the ebb-tide.

3

It avails not, time nor place—distance avails not,
I am with you, you men and women of a generation, or ever so
many generations hence,
Just as you feel when you look on the river and sky, so I felt,
Just as any of you is one of a living crowd, I was one of a crowd,
Just as you are refresh'd by the gladness of the river and the
bright flow, I was refresh'd,
Just as you stand and lean on the rail, yet hurry with the swift
current, I stood yet was hurried,
Just as you look on the numberless masts of ships and the thick-
stemm'd pipes of steamboats, I look'd.

I too many and many a time cross'd the river of old,
Watched the Twelfth-month sea-gulls, saw them high in the air
floating with motionless wings, oscillating their bodies,
Saw how the glistening yellow lit up parts of their bodies and
left the rest in strong shadow,
Saw the slow-wheeling circles and the gradual edging toward
the south,
Saw the reflection of the summer sky in the water,
Had my eyes dazzled by the shimmering track of beams,
Look'd at the fine centrifugal spokes of light round the shape
of my head in the sunlit water,
Look'd on the haze on the hills southward and south-westward,
Look'd on the vapor as it flew in fleeces tinged with violet,
Look'd toward the lower bay to notice the vessels arriving,
Saw their approach, saw aboard those that were near me,
Saw the white sails of schooners and sloops, saw the ships at
anchor,

The sailors at work in the rigging or out astride the spars,
The round masts, the swinging motion of the hulls, the slender
    serpentine pennants,
The large and small steamers in motion, the pilots in their pilot-
    houses,
The white wake left by the passage, the quick tremulous whirl
    of the wheels,
The flags of all nations, the falling of them at sunset,
The scallop-edged waves in the twilight, the ladled cups, the
    frolicsome crests and glistening,
The stretch afar growing dimmer and dimmer, the gray walls
    of the granite storehouses by the docks,
On the river the shadowy group, the big steam-tug closely
    flank'd on each side by the barges, the hayboat, the be-
    lated lighter,
On the neighboring shore the fires from the foundry chimneys
    burning high and glaringly into the night,
Casting their flicker of black contrasted with wild red and yel-
    low light over the tops of houses, and down into the
    clefts of streets.

.   .   .   .

5

What is it then between us?
What is the count of the scores or hundreds of years between us?

Whatever it is, it avails not—distance avails not, and place
    avails not,
I too lived, Brooklyn of ample hills was mine,
I too walk'd the streets of Manhattan island, and bathed in the
    waters around it,
I too felt the curious abrupt questionings stir within me.
In the day among crowds of people sometimes they came upon
    me,
In my walks home late at night or as I lay in my bed they came
    upon me,

I too had been struck from the float forever held in solution,
I too had receiv'd identity by my body,
That I was I knew was of my body, and what I should be I knew
I should be of my body.

. . . .

9

Flow on, river! flow with the flood-tide, and ebb with the ebb-
tide!
Frolic on, crested and scallop-edg'd waves!
Gorgeous clouds of the sunset! drench with your splendor me,
or the men and women generations after me!
Cross from shore to shore, countless crowds of passengers!
Stand up, tall masts of Mannahatta! stand up, beautiful hills of
Brooklyn!
Throb, baffled and curious brain! throw out questions and an-
swers!
Suspend here and everywhere, eternal float of solution!
Gaze, loving and thirsting eyes, in the house or street or public
assembly!
Sound out, voices of young men; loudly and musically call me
by my nighest name!
Live, old life! play the part that looks back on the actor or ac-
tress!
Play the old role, the role that is great or small according as
one makes it!
Consider, you who peruse me, whether I may not in unknown
ways be looking upon you;
Be firm, rail over the river, to support those who lean idly, yet
haste with the hasting current;
Fly on, sea-birds! fly sideways, or wheel in large circles high in
the air;
Receive the summer sky, you water, and faithfully hold it
till all downcast eyes have time to take it from you!
Diverge, fine spokes of light, from the shape of my head, or
any one's head, in the sunlit water!

Come on, ships from the lower bay! pass up or down, white-
    sail'd schooners, sloops, lighters!
Flaunt away, flags of all nations! be duly lower'd at sunset!
Burn high you fires, foundry chimneys! cast black shadows at
    nightfall! cast red and yellow light over the tops of the
    houses!
Appearances, now or henceforth, indicate what you are,
You necessary film, continue to envelop the soul,
About my body for me, and your body for you, be hung our
    divinest aromas,
Thrive, cities—bring your freight, bring your shows, ample
    and sufficient rivers,
Expand, being than which none else is perhaps more spiritual,
Keep your places, objects than which none else is more lasting.

You have waited, you always wait, you dumb, beautiful minis-
    ters,
We receive you with free sense at last, and are insatiate hence-
    forward,
Not you any more shall be able to foil us, or withhold your-
    selves from us,
We use you, and do not cast you aside—we plant you perma-
    nently within us,
We fathom you not—we love you—there is perfection in you
    also,
You furnish your parts toward eternity,
Great or small, you furnish your parts toward the soul.

Song of the Redwood-Tree

1

A California song,
A prophecy and indirection, a thought impalpable to breathe
    as air,
A chorus of dryads, fading, departing, or hamadryads depart-
    ing,
A murmuring, fateful, giant voice, out of the earth and sky,
Voice of a mighty dying tree in the redwood forest dense.

Farewell my brethren,
Farewell O earth and sky, farewell ye neighboring waters,
My time has ended, my term has come.

Along the northern coast,
Just back from the rock-bound shore and the caves,
In the saline air from the sea in the Mendocino country,
With the surge for base and accompaniment low and hoarse,
With crackling blows of axes sounding musically driven by
    strong arms,
Riven deep by the sharp tongues of the axes, there in the red-
    wood forest dense,
I heard the mighty tree its death-chant chanting.

The choppers heard not, the camp shanties echoed not,
The quick-ear'd teamsters and chain and jack-screw men heard
    not,
As the wood-spirits came from their haunts of a thousand years
    to join the refrain,
But in my soul I plainly heard.

Murmuring out of its myriad leaves,
Down from its lofty top rising two hundred feet high,
Out of its stalwart trunk and limbs, out of its foot-thick bark,
That chant of the seasons and time, chant not of the past only
    but the future.

36

You untold life of me,
And all you venerable and innocent joys,
Perennial hardy life of me with joys 'mid rain and many a sum-
    mer sun,
And the white snows and night and the wild winds;
O the great patient rugged joys, my soul's strong joys unreck'd
    by man,
(For know I bear the soul befitting me, I too have conscious-
    ness, identity,
And all the rocks and mountains have, and all the earth,)
Joys of the life befitting me and brothers mine,
Our time, our term has come.

Nor yield we mournfully majestic brothers,
We who have grandly fill'd our time;
With Nature's calm content, with tacit huge delight,
We welcome what we wrought for through the past,
And leave the field for them.

For them predicted long,
For a superber race, they too to grandly fill their time,
For them we abdicate, in them ourselves ye forest kings!
In them these skies and airs, these mountain peaks, Shasta,
    Nevadas,
These huge precipitous cliffs, this amplitude, these valleys, far
    Yosemite,
To be in them absorb'd, assimilated.

Then to a loftier strain,
Still prouder, more ecstatic rose the chant,
As if the heirs, the deities of the West,
Joining with master-tongue bore part.

Not wan from Asia's fetiches,
Nor red from Europe's old dynastic slaughter-house,
(Area of murder-plots of thrones, with scent left yet of wars
    and scaffolds everywhere,)
But come from Nature's long and harmless throes, peacefully
    builded thence,

These virgin lands, lands of the Western shore,
To the new culminating man, to you, the empire new,
You promis'd long, we pledge, we dedicate.

You occult deep volitions,
You average spiritual manhood, purpose of all, pois'd on your-
self, giving not taking law,
You womanhood divine, mistress and source of all, whence
life and love and aught that comes from life and love,
You unseen moral essence of all the vast materials of America,
(age upon age working in death the same as life,)
You that, sometimes known, oftener unknown, really shape
and mould the New World, adjusting it to Time and
Space,
You hidden national will lying in your abysms, conceal'd but
ever alert,
You past and present purposes tenaciously pursued, may-be un-
conscious of yourselves,
Unswerv'd by all the passing errors, perturbations of the sur-
face;
You vital, universal, deathless germs, beneath all creeds, arts,
statutes, literatures,
Here build your homes for good, establish here, these areas en-
tire, lands of the Western shore,
We pledge, we dedicate to you.

For man of you, your characteristic race,
Here may he hardy, sweet, gigantic grow, here tower propor-
tionate to Nature,
Here climb the vast pure spaces unconfined, uncheck'd by wall
or roof,
Here laugh with storm or sun, here joy, here patiently inure,
Here heed himself, unfold himself, (not others' formulas heed,)
here fill his time,
38 *To duty fall, to aid, unreck'd at last,*
To disappear, to serve.

Thus on the northern coast,
In the echo of teamsters' calls and the clinking chains, and the
    music of choppers' axes,
The falling trunk and limbs, the crash, the muffled shriek, the
    groan,
Such words combined from the redwood-tree, as of voices ec-
    static, ancient and rustling,
The century-lasting, unseen dryads, singing, withdrawing,
All their recesses of forests and mountains leaving,
From the Cascade range to the Wasatch, or Idaho far, or Utah,
To the deities of the modern henceforth yielding,
The chorus and indications, the vistas of coming humanity, the
    settlements, features all,
In the Mendocino woods I caught.

2

The flashing and golden pageant of California,
The sudden and gorgeous drama, the sunny and ample lands,
The long and varied stretch from Puget sound to Colorado
    south,
Lands bathed in sweeter, rarer, healthier air, valleys and
    mountain cliffs,
The fields of Nature long prepared and fallow, the silent, cyclic
    chemistry,
The slow and steady ages plodding, the unoccupied surface
    ripening, the rich ores forming beneath;
At last the New arriving, assuming, taking possession,
A swarming and busy race settling and organizing everywhere,
Ships coming in from the whole round world, and going out to
    the whole world,
To India and China and Australia and the thousand island
    paradises of the Pacific,
Populous cities, the latest inventions, the steamers on the rivers,
    the railroads, with many a thrifty farm, with machin-
    ery,

And wool and wheat and the grape, and diggings of yellow
    gold.

3

But more in you than these, lands of the Western shore,
(These but the means, the implements, the standing-ground,)
I see in you, certain to come, the promise of thousands of years,
    till now deferr'd,
Promis'd to be fulfill'd, our common kind, the race.

The new society at last, proportionate to Nature,
In man of you, more than your mountain peaks or stalwart
    trees imperial,
In woman more, far more, than all your gold or vines, or even
    vital air.

Fresh come, to a new world indeed, yet long prepared,
I see the genius of the modern, child of the real and ideal,
Clearing the ground for broad humanity, the true America,
    heir of the past so grand,
To build a grander future.

Facing West from California's Shores

Facing west from California's shores,
Inquiring, tireless, seeking what is yet unfound,
I, a child, very old, over waves, towards the house of maternity,
      the land of migrations, look afar,
Look off the shores of my Western sea, the circle almost cir-
      cled;
For starting westward from Hindustan, from the vales of Kash-
      mere,
From Asia, from the north, from the God, the sage, and the hero,
From the south, from the flowery peninsulas and the spice is-
      lands,
Long having wander'd since, round the earth having wander'd,
Now I face home again, very pleas'd and joyous,
(But where is what I started for so long ago?
And why is it yet unfound?)

EARTH, SEA, AND SKY

This Compost

Something startles me where I thought I was safest,
I withdraw from the still woods I loved,
I will not go now on the pastures to walk,
I will not strip the clothes from my body to meet my lover the
    sea,
I will not touch my flesh to the earth as to other flesh to renew
    me.

O how can it be that the ground itself does not sicken?
How can you be alive you growths of spring?
How can you furnish health you blood of herbs, roots, orchards,
    grain?
Are they not continually putting distemper'd corpses within
    you?
Is not every continent work'd over and over with sour dead?

Where have you disposed of their carcasses?
Those drunkards and gluttons of so many generations?
Where have you drawn off all the foul liquid and meat?
I do not see any of it upon you to-day, or perhaps I am deceiv'd,
I will run a furrow with my plough, I will press my spade
    through the sod and turn it up underneath,
I am sure I shall expose some of the foul meat.

2

Behold this compost! behold it well!
Perhaps every mite has once form'd part of a sick person—yet
    behold!
The grass of spring covers the prairies,
The bean bursts noiselessly through the mould in the garden,
The delicate spear of the onion pierces upward,
The apple-buds cluster together on the apple-branches,
The resurrection of the wheat appears with pale visage out of
    its graves,
The tinge awakes over the willow-tree and the mulberry-tree,

The he-birds carol mornings and evenings while the she-birds
    sit on their nests,
The young of poultry break through the hatch'd eggs,
The new-born of animals appear, the calf is dropt from the cow,
    the colt from the mare,
Out of its little hill faithfully rise the potato's dark green leaves,
Out of its hill rises the yellow maize-stalk, the lilacs bloom in
    the dooryards,
The summer growth is innocent and disdainful above all those
    strata of sour dead.

What chemistry!
That the winds are really not infectious,
That this is no cheat, this transparent green-wash of the sea
    which is so amorous after me,
That it is safe to allow it to lick my naked body all over with its
    tongues,
That it will not endanger me with the fevers that have depos-
    ited themselves in it,
That all is clean forever and forever,
That the cool drink from the well tastes so good,
That blackberries are so flavorous and juicy,
That the fruits of the apple-orchard and the orange-orchard,
    that melons, grapes, peaches, plums, will none of them
    poison me,
That when I recline on the grass I do not catch any disease,
Though probably every spear of grass rises out of what was
    once a catching disease.

Now I am terrified at the Earth, it is that calm and patient,
It grows such sweet things out of such corruptions,
It turns harmless and stainless on its axis, with such endless
    successions of diseas'd corpses,
It distills such exquisite winds out of such infused fetor,
It renews with such unwitting looks its prodigal, annual, sump-
    tuous crops,
It gives such divine materials to men, and accepts such leavings
    from them at last.

Miracles

Why, who makes much of a miracle?
As to me I know of nothing else but miracles,
Whether I walk the streets of Manhattan,
Or dart my sight over the roofs of houses toward the sky,
Or wade with naked feet along the beach just in the edge of
     the water,
Or stand under trees in the woods,
Or talk by day with any one I love, or sleep in the bed at night
     with any one I love,
Or sit at table at dinner with the rest,
Or look at strangers opposite me riding in the car,
Or watch honey-bees busy around the hive of a summer fore-
     noon,
Or animals feeding in the fields,
Or birds, or the wonderfulness of insects in the air,
Or the wonderfulness of the sundown, or of stars shining so
     quiet and bright,
Or the exquisite delicate thin curve of the new moon in spring;
These with the rest, one and all, are to me miracles,
The whole referring, yet each distinct and in its place.

To me every hour of the light and dark is a miracle,
Every cubic inch of space is a miracle,
Every square yard of the surface of the earth is spread with the
     same,
Every foot of the interior swarms with the same.

To me the sea is a continual miracle,
The fishes that swim—the rocks—the motion of the waves—
     the ships with men in them,
What stranger miracles are there?

A Song for Occupations

. . . .

3

The sun and stars that float in the open air,
The apple-shaped earth and we upon it, surely the drift of them
    is something grand,
I do not know what it is except that it is grand, and that it is hap-
    piness,
And that the enclosing purport of us here is not a speculation or
    bon-mot or reconnoissance,
And that it is not something which by luck may turn out well for
    us, and without luck must be a failure for us,
And not something which may yet be retracted in a certain con-
    tingency.

The light and shade, the curious sense of body and identity, the
    greed that with perfect complaisance devours all things,
The endless pride and outstretching of man, unspeakable joys
    and sorrows,
The wonder every one sees in every one else he sees, and the
    wonders that fill each minute of time forever,
What have you reckon'd them for, camerado?
Have you reckon'd them for your trade or farm-work? or for
    the profits of your store?
Or to achieve yourself a position? or to fill a gentleman's lei-
    sure, or a lady's leisure?

Have you reckon'd that the landscape took substance and form
    that it might be painted in a picture?
Or men and women that they might be written of, and songs
    sung?
Or the attraction of gravity, and the great laws and harmoni-
    ous combinations and the fluids of the air, as subjects
    for the savans?
Or the brown land and the blue sea for maps and charts?

Or the stars to be put in constellations and named fancy
   names?
Or that the growth of seeds is for agricultural tables, or agri-
   culture itself?

Old institutions, these arts, libraries, legends, collections, and
   the practice handed along in manufactures, will we
   rate them so high?
Will we rate our cash and business high? I have no objection,
I rate them as high as the highest—then a child born of a
   woman and man I rate beyond all rate.

We thought our Union grand, and our Constitution grand,
I do not say they are not grand and good, for they are,
I am this day just as much in love with them as you,
Then I am in love with You, and with all my fellows upon the
   earth.

We consider bibles and religions divine—I do not say they are
   not divine,
I say they have all grown out of you, and may grow out of you
   still,
It is not they who give the life, it is you who give the life,
Leaves are not more shed from the trees, or trees from the earth,
   than they are shed out of you.

Thou Orb Aloft Full-Dazzling

Thou orb aloft full-dazzling! thou hot October noon!
Flooding with sheeny light the gray beach sand,
The sibilant near sea with vistas far and foam,
And tawny streaks and shades and spreading blue;
O sun of noon refulgent! my special word to thee.

Hear me illustrious!
Thy lover me, for always I have loved thee,
Even as basking babe, then happy boy alone by some wood
  edge, thy touching-distant beams enough,
Or man matured, or young or old, as now to thee I launch my
  invocation.

(Thou canst not with thy dumbness me deceive,
I know before the fitting man all Nature yields,
Thought answering not in words, the skies, trees, hear his voice
  —and thou O sun,
As for thy throes, thy perturbations, sudden breaks and shafts
  of flame gigantic,
I understand them, I know those flames, those perturbations
  well.)

Thou that with fructifying heat and light,
O'er myriad farms, o'er lands and waters North and South,
O'er Mississippi's endless course, o'er Texas' grassy plains,
  Kanada's woods,
O'er all the globe that turns its face to thee shining in space,
Thou that impartially infoldest all, not only continents, seas,
Thou that to grapes and weeds and little wild flowers givest so
  liberally,
Shed, shed thyself on mine and me, with but a fleeting ray out
  of thy million millions,
Strike through these chants.

Nor only launch thy subtle dazzle and thy strength for these,
Prepare the later afternoon of me myself—prepare my length-
  ening shadows,
Prepare my starry nights.

Song of the Open Road

3

You air that serves me with breath to speak!
You objects that call from diffusion my meanings and give
     them shape!
You light that wraps me and all things in delicate equable
     showers!
You paths worn in the irregular hollows by the roadsides!
I believe you are latent with unseen existences, you are so dear
     to me.

You flagg'd walks of the cities! you strong curbs at the edges!
You ferries! you planks and posts of wharves! you timber-lined
     sides! you distant ships!
You rows of houses! you window-pierc'd façades! you roofs!
You porches and entrances! you copings and iron guards!
You windows whose transparent shells might expose so much!
You doors and ascending steps! you arches!
You gray stones of interminable pavements! you trodden
     crossings!
From all that has touch'd you I believe you have imparted to
     yourselves, and now would impart the same secretly
     to me,
From the living and the dead you have peopled your impassive
     surfaces, and the spirits thereof would be evident and
     amicable with me.

. . . .

4

The earth expanding right hand and left hand,
The picture alive, every part in its best light,
The music falling in where it is wanted, and stopping where it
     is not wanted,
The cheerful voice of the public road, the gay fresh sentiment
     of the road.

O highway I travel, do you say to me *Do not leave me?*
Do you say *Venture not—if you leave me you are lost?*
Do you say *I am already prepared, I am well-beaten and un-
denied, adhere to me?*

O public road, I say back I am not afraid to leave you, yet I
love you,
You express me better than I can express myself,
You shall be more to me than my poem.

I think heroic deeds were all conceiv'd in the open air, and all
free poems also,
I think I could stop here myself and do miracles,
I think whatever I shall meet on the road I shall like, and who-
ever beholds me shall like me,
I think whoever I see must be happy.

Unseen Buds

Unseen buds, infinite, hidden well,
Under the snow and ice, under the darkness, in every square or
cubic inch,
Germinal, exquisite, in delicate lace, microscopic, unborn,
Like babes in wombs, latent, folded, compact, sleeping;
Billions of billions, and trillions of trillions of them waiting,
(On earth and in the sea—the universe—the stars there in the
heavens,)
Urging slowly, surely forward, forming endless,
And waiting ever more, forever more behind.

Give Me the Splendid Silent Sun

1

Give me the splendid silent sun with all his beams full-dazzling,
Give me juicy autumnal fruit ripe and red from the orchard,
Give me a field where the unmow'd grass grows,
Give me an arbor, give me the trellis'd grape,
Give me fresh corn and wheat, give me serene-moving animals
    teaching content,
Give me nights perfectly quiet as on high plateaus west of the
    Mississippi, and I looking up at the stars,
Give me odorous at sunrise a garden of beautiful flowers where
    I can walk undisturb'd,
Give me for marriage a sweet-breath'd woman of whom I
    should never tire,
Give me a perfect child, give me away aside from the noise of
    the world a rural domestic life,
Give me to warble spontaneous songs recluse by myself, for
    my own ears only,
Give me solitude, give me Nature, give me again O Nature
    your primal sanities!

These demanding to have them, (tired with ceaseless excite-
    ment, and rack'd by the war-strife,)
These to procure incessantly asking, rising in cries from my
    heart,
While yet incessantly asking still I adhere to my city,
Day upon day and year upon year O city, walking your streets,
Where you hold me enchain'd a certain time refusing to give
    me up,
Yet giving to make me glutted, enrich'd of soul, you give me
    forever faces;
(O I see what I sought to escape, confronting, reversing my
    cries,
I see my own soul trampling down what is ask'd for.)

Keep your splendid silent sun,
Keep your woods O Nature, and the quiet places by the woods,
Keep your fields of clover and timothy, and your corn-fields
      and orchards,
Keep the blossoming buckwheat fields where the Ninth-month
      bees hum;
Give me faces and streets, give me these phantoms incessant
      and endless along the trottoirs!
Give me interminable eyes—give me women—give me com-
      rades and lovers by the thousand!
Let me see new ones every day—let me hold new ones by the
      hand every day!
Give me such shows—give me the streets of Manhattan!
Give me Broadway, with the soldiers marching—give me the
      sound of the trumpets and drums!
(The soldiers in companies or regiments—some starting away,
      flush'd and reckless,
Some, their time up, returning with thinn'd ranks, young, yet
      very old, worn, marching, noticing nothing;)
Give me the shores and wharves heavy-fringed with black
      ships!
O such for me! O an intense life, full to repletion and varied!
The life of the theatre, bar-room, huge hotel, for me!
The saloon of the steamer! the crowded excursion for me! the
      torchlight procession!
The dense brigade bound for the war, with high piled military
      wagons following;
People, endless, streaming, with strong voices, passions, pag-
      eants,
Manhattan streets with their powerful throbs, with beating
      drums as now,
The endless and noisy chorus, the rustle and clank of muskets,
      (even the sight of the wounded,)
Manhattan crowds, with their turbulent musical chorus!
Manhattan faces and eyes forever for me.

Out of the Cradle Endlessly Rocking

Out of the cradle endlessly rocking,
Out of the mocking-bird's throat, the musical shuttle,
Out of the Ninth-month midnight,
Over the sterile sands and the fields beyond, where the child
leaving his bed wander'd alone, bareheaded, barefoot,
Down from the shower'd halo,
Up from the mystic play of shadows twining and twisting as if
they were alive,
Out from the patches of briers and blackberries,
From the memories of the bird that chanted to me,
From your memories sad brother, from the fitful risings and
fallings I heard,
From under that yellow half-moon late-risen and swollen as if
with tears,
From those beginning notes of yearning and love there in the
mist,
From the thousand responses of my heart never to cease,
From the myriad thence-arous'd words,
From the word stronger and more delicious than any,
From such as now they start the scene revisiting,
As a flock, twittering, rising, or overhead passing,
Borne hither, ere all eludes me, hurriedly,
A man, yet by these tears a little boy again,
Throwing myself on the sand, confronting the waves,
I, chanter of pains and joys, uniter of here and hereafter,
Taking all hints to use them, but swiftly leaping beyond them,
A reminiscence sing.

Once, Paumanok,
When the lilac-scent was in the air and Fifth-month grass was
growing,
Up this seashore in some briers,
Two feather'd guests from Alabama, two together,
And their nest, and four light-green eggs spotted with brown,
And every day the he-bird to and fro near at hand,

And every day the she-bird crouch'd on her nest, silent, with
      bright eyes,
And every day I, a curious boy, never too close, never disturb-
      ing them,
Cautiously peering, absorbing, translating.

Shine! shine! shine!
Pour down your warmth, great sun!
While we bask, we two together.

Two together!
Winds blow south, or winds blow north,
Day come white, or night come black,
Home, or rivers and mountains from home,
Singing all time, minding no time,
While we two keep together.

Till of a sudden,
May-be kill'd, unknown to her mate,
One forenoon the she-bird crouch'd not on the nest,
Nor return'd that afternoon, nor the next,
Nor ever appear'd again.

And thenceforward all summer in the sound of the sea,
And at night under the full of the moon in calmer weather,
Over the hoarse surging of the sea,
Or flitting from brier to brier by day,
I saw, I heard at intervals the remaining one, the he-bird,
The solitary guest from Alabama.

Blow! blow! blow!
Blow up sea-winds along Paumanok's shore;
I wait and I wait till you blow my mate to me.

Yes, when the stars glisten'd,
All night long on the prong of a moss-scallop'd stake,
Down almost amid the slapping waves,
Sat the lone singer wonderful causing tears.

He call'd on his mate,
He pour'd forth the meanings which I of all men know.

Yes my brother I know,
The rest might not, but I have treasur'd every note,
For more than once dimly down to the beach gliding,
Silent, avoiding the moonbeams, blending myself with the
  shadows,
Recalling now the obscure shapes, the echoes, the sounds and
  sights after their sorts,
The white arms out in the breakers tirelessly tossing,
I, with bare feet, a child, the wind wafting my hair,
Listen'd long and long.

Listen'd to keep, to sing, now translating the notes,
Following you my brother.

Soothe! soothe! soothe!
Close on its wave soothes the wave behind,
And again another behind embracing and lapping, every one
  close,
But my love soothes not me, not me.

Low hangs the moon, it rose late,
It is lagging—O I think it is heavy with love, with love.

O madly the sea pushes upon the land,
With love, with love.

O night! do I not see my love fluttering out among the breakers?
What is that little black thing I see there in the white?

Loud! loud! loud!
Loud I call to you, my love!
High and clear I shoot my voice over the waves,
Surely you must know who is here, is here,
You must know whom I am, my love.

56

Low-hanging moon!
What is that dusky spot in your brown yellow?

O it is the shape, the shape of my mate!
O moon do not keep her from me any longer.

Land! land! O land!
Whichever way I turn, O I think you could give me my mate
*   back again if you only would,*
For I am almost sure I see her dimly whichever way I look.

O rising stars!
Perhaps the one I want so much will rise, will rise with some
*   of you.*

O throat! O trembling throat!
Sound clearer through the atmosphere!
Pierce the woods, the earth,
Somewhere listening to catch you must be the one I want.

Shake out carols!
Solitary here, the night's carols!
Carols of lonesome love! death's carols!
Carols under that lagging, yellow, waning moon!
O under the moon where she droops almost down into the sea!
O reckless despairing carols.

But soft! sink low!
Soft! let me just murmur,
And do you wait a moment you husky-nois'd sea,
For somewhere I believe I heard my mate responding to me,
So faint, I must be still, be still to listen,
But not altogether still, for then she might not come immedi-
*   ately to me.*

Hither my love!
Here I am! here!
With this just-sustain'd note I announce myself to you,
This gentle call is for you my love, for you.

Do not be decoy'd elsewhere,
That is the whistle of the wind, it is not my voice,

That is the fluttering, the fluttering of the spray,
Those are the shadows of leaves.

O darkness! O in vain!
O I am very sick and sorrowful.

O brown halo in the sky near the moon, drooping upon the sea!
O troubled reflection in the sea!

O throat! O throbbing heart!
And I singing uselessly, uselessly all the night.

O past! O happy life! O songs of joy!
In the air, in the woods, over fields,
Loved! loved! loved! loved! loved!
But my mate no more, no more with me!
We two together no more.

The aria sinking,
All else continuing, the stars shining,
The winds blowing, the notes of the bird continuous echoing,
With angry moans the fierce old mother incessantly moaning,
On the sands of Paumanok's shore gray and rustling,
The yellow half-moon enlarged, sagging down, drooping, the
    face of the sea almost touching,
The boy ecstatic, with his bare feet the waves, with his hair the
    atmosphere dallying,
The love in the heart long pent, now loose, now at last tumul-
    tuously bursting,
The aria's meaning, the ears, the soul, swiftly depositing,
The strange tears down the cheeks coursing,
The colloquy there, the trio, each uttering,
The undertone, the savage old mother incessantly crying,
To the boy's soul's questions sullenly timing, some drown'd
    secret hissing,
To the outsetting bard.

58

Demon or bird! (said the boy's soul,)
Is it indeed toward your mate you sing? or is it really to me?

For I, that was a child, my tongue's use sleeping, now I have
heard you,
Now in a moment I know what I am for, I awake,
And already a thousand singers, a thousand songs, clearer,
louder and more sorrowful than yours,
A thousand warbling echoes have started to life within me,
never to die.

O you singer solitary, singing by yourself, projecting me,
O solitary me listening, never more shall I cease perpetuating
you,
Never more shall I escape, never more the reverberations,
Never more the cries of unsatisfied love be absent from me,
Never again leave me to be the peaceful child I was before
what there in the night,
By the sea under the yellow and sagging moon,
The messenger there arous'd, the fire, the sweet hell within,
The unknown want, the destiny of me.

O give me the clew! (it lurks in the night here somewhere,)
O if I am to have so much, let me have more!

A word then, (for I will conquer it,)
The word final, superior to all,
Subtle, sent up—what is it?—I listen;
Are you whispering it, and have been all the time, you sea
waves?
Is that it from your liquid rims and wet sands?

Whereto answering, the sea,
Delaying not, hurrying not,
Whisper'd me through the night, and very plainly before day-
break,
Lisp'd to me the low and delicious word death,
And again death, death, death, death,
Hissing melodious, neither like the bird nor like my arous'd
child's heart,
But edging near as privately for me rustling at my feet,

Creeping thence steadily up to my ears and laving me softly all
       over,
Death, death, death, death, death.

Which I do not forget,
But fuse the song of my dusky demon and brother,
That he sang to me in the moonlight on Paumanok's gray beach,
With the thousand responsive songs at random,
My own songs awaked from that hour,
And with them the key, the word up from the waves,
The word of the sweetest song and all songs,
That strong and delicious word which, creeping to my feet,
(Or like some old crone rocking the cradle, swathed in sweet
      garments, bending aside,)
The sea whisper'd me.

On the Beach at Night

On the beach at night,
Stands a child with her father,
Watching the east, the autumn sky.

Up through the darkness,
While ravening clouds, the burial clouds, in black masses
      spreading,

Lower sullen and fast athwart and down the sky,
Amid a transparent clear belt of ether yet left in the east,
Ascends large and calm the lord-star Jupiter,
And nigh at hand, only a very little above,
Swim the delicate sisters the Pleiades.

From the beach the child holding the hand of her father,
Those burial clouds that lower victorious soon to devour all,
Watching, silently weeps.

Weep not, child,
Weep not, my darling,
With these kisses let me remove your tears,
The ravening clouds shall not long be victorious,
They shall not long possess the sky, they devour the stars only
        in apparition,
Jupiter shall emerge, be patient, watch again another night, the
        Pleiades shall emerge,
They are immortal, all those stars both silvery and golden shall
        shine out again,
The great stars and the little ones shall shine out again, they en-
        dure,
The vast immortal suns and the long-enduring pensive moons
        shall again shine.

Then dearest child mournest thou only for Jupiter?
Considerest thou alone the burial of the stars?

Something there is,
(With my lips soothing thee, adding I whisper,
I give thee the first suggestion, the problem and indirection,)
Something there is more immortal even than the stars,
(Many the burials, many the days and nights, passing away,)
Something that shall endure longer even than lustrous Jupiter,
Longer than sun or any revolving satellite,
Or the radiant sisters the Pleiades.

Aboard at a Ship's Helm

Aboard at a ship's helm,
A young steersman steering with care.

Through fog on a sea-coast dolefully ringing,
An ocean-bell—O a warning bell, rock'd by the waves.

O you give good notice indeed, you bell by the sea-reefs ringing,
Ringing, ringing, to warn the ship from its wreck-place.

For as on the alert O steersman, you mind the loud admonition,
The bows turn, the freighted ship tacking speeds away under
her gray sails,
The beautiful and noble ship with all her precious wealth speeds
away gayly and safe.

But O the ship, the immortal ship! O ship aboard the ship!
Ship of the body, ship of the soul, voyaging, voyaging, voyaging.

Song for All Seas, All Ships

1

To-day a rude brief recitative,
Of ships sailing the seas, each with its special flag or ship-signal,
Of unnamed heroes in the ships—of waves spreading and
spreading far as the eye can reach,
Of dashing spray, and the winds piping and blowing,
And out of these a chant for the sailors of all nations,
Fitful, like a surge.

Of sea-captains young or old, and the mates, and of all in-
     trepid sailors,
Of the few, very choice, taciturn, whom fate can never surprise
     nor death dismay,
Pick'd sparingly without noise by thee old ocean, chosen by
     thee,
Thou sea that pickest and cullest the race in time, and unitest
     nations,
Suckled by thee, old husky nurse, embodying thee,
Indomitable, untamed as thee.

(Ever the heroes on water or on land, by ones or twos appear-
     ing,
Ever the stock preserv'd and never lost, though rare, enough
     for seed preserv'd.)

2

Flaunt out O sea your separate flags of nations!
Flaunt out visible as ever the various ship-signals!
But do you reserve especially for yourself and for the soul of
     man one flag above all the rest,
A spiritual woven signal for all nations, emblem of man elate
     above death,
Token of all brave captains and all intrepid sailors and mates,
And all that went down doing their duty,
Reminiscent of them, twined from all intrepid captains young
     or old,
A pennant universal, subtly waving all time, o'er all brave
     sailors,
All seas, all ships.

To the Man-of-War-Bird

Thou who has slept all night upon the storm,
Waking renew'd on thy prodigious pinions,
(Burst the wild storm? above it thou ascended'st,
And rested on the sky, thy slave that cradled thee,)
Now a blue point, far, far in heaven floating,
As to the light emerging here on deck I watch thee,
(Myself a speck, a point on the world's floating vast.)
Far, far at sea,
After the night's fierce drifts have strewn the shore with wrecks,
With re-appearing day as now so happy and serene,
The rosy and elastic dawn, the flashing sun,
The limpid spread of air cerulean,
Thou also re-appearest.

Thou born to match the gale, (thou art all wings,)
To cope with heaven and earth and sea and hurricane,
Thou ship of air that never furl'st thy sails,
Days, even weeks untired and onward, through spaces, realms
    gyrating,
At dusk that look'st on Senegal, at morn America,
That sport'st amid the lightning-flash and thunder-cloud,
In them, in thy experiences, had'st thou my soul,
What joys! what joys were thine!

The Dalliance of the Eagles

Skirting the river road, (my forenoon walk, my rest,)
Skyward in air a sudden muffled sound, the dalliance of the
  eagles,
The rushing amorous contact high in space together,
The clinching interlocking claws, a living, fierce, gyrating
  wheel,
Four beating wings, two beaks, a swirling mass tight grappling,
In tumbling turning clustering loops, straight downward falling,
Till o'er the river pois'd, the twain yet one, a moment's lull,
A motionless still balance in the air, then parting, talons loos-
  ing,
Upward again on slow-firm pinions slanting, their separate di-
  verse flight,
She hers, he his, pursuing.

I,
WALT
WHITMAN

Come, said my Soul,
Such verses for my Body let us write, (for we are one,)
That should I after death invisibly return,
Or, long, long hence, in other spheres,
There to some group of mates the chants resuming,
(Tallying Earth's soil, trees, winds, tumultuous waves,)
Ever with pleas'd smile I may keep on,
Ever and ever yet the verses owning—as, first, I here and now
Signing for Soul and Body, set to them my name,

Walt Whitman

Thou Reader

Thou reader throbbest life and pride and love the same as I,
Therefore for thee the following chants.

One's-Self I Sing

One's-self I sing, a simple separate person,
Yet utter the word Democratic, the word En-Masse.

Of physiology from top to toe I sing,
Not physiognomy alone nor brain alone is worthy for the Muse,
I say the Form complete is worthier far,
The Female equally with the Male I sing.

Of Life immense in passion, pulse, and power,
Cheerful, for freest action form'd under the laws divine,
The Modern Man I sing.

Beginning My Studies

Beginning my studies the first step pleas'd me so much,
The mere fact consciousness, these forms, the power of motion,
The least insect or animal, the senses, eyesight, love,
The first step I say awed me and pleas'd me so much,
I have hardly gone and hardly wish'd to go any farther,
But stop and loiter all the time to sing it in ecstatic songs.

There Was a Child Went Forth

There was a child went forth every day,
And the first object he look'd upon, that object he became,
And that object became part of him for the day or a certain
       part of the day,
Or for many years or stretching cycles of years.

The early lilacs became part of this child,
And grass and white and red morning-glories, and white and
       red clover, and the song of the phoebe-bird,
And the Third-month lambs and the sow's pink-faint litter, and
       the mare's foal and the cow's calf,
And the noisy brood of the barnyard or by the mire of the
       pond-side,
And the fish suspending themselves so curiously below there,
       and the beautiful curious liquid,
And the water-plants with their graceful flat heads, all became
       part of him.

The field-sprouts of Fourth-month and Fifth-month became
       part of him,
Winter-grain sprouts and those of the light-yellow corn, and
       the esculent roots of the garden,
And the apple-trees cover'd with blossoms and the fruit after-
       ward, and wood-berries, and the commonest weeds by
       the road,
And the old drunkard staggering home from the outhouse of
       the tavern whence he had lately risen,
And the schoolmistress that pass'd on her way to the school,
And the friendly boys that pass'd and the quarrelsome boys,
And the tidy and fresh-cheek'd girls, and the barefoot Negro
       boy and girl,
And all the changes of city and country wherever he went.

His own parents, he that had father'd him and she that had
       conceiv'd him in her womb and birth'd him,
They gave this child more of themselves than that,
They gave him afterward every day, they became part of him.

The mother at home quietly placing the dishes on the supper-table,

The mother with mild words, clean her cap and gown, a wholesome odor falling off her person and clothes as she walks by,

The father, strong, self-sufficient, manly, mean, anger'd, unjust,

The blow, the quick loud word, the tight bargain, the crafty lure,

The family usages, the language, the company, the furniture, the yearning and swelling heart,

Affection that will not be gainsay'd, the sense of what is real, the thought if after all it should prove unreal,

The doubts of day-time and the doubts of night-time, the curious whether and how,

Whether that which appears so is so, or is it all flashes and specks?

Men and women crowding fast in the streets, if they are not flashes and specks what are they?

The streets themselves and the façades of houses, and goods in the windows,

Vehicles, teams, the heavy-plank'd wharves, the huge crossing at the ferries,

The village on the highland seen from afar at sunset, the river between,

Shadows, aureola and mist, the light falling on roofs and gables of white or brown two miles off,

The schooner near by sleepily dropping down the tide, the little boat slack-tow'd astern,

The hurrying tumbling waves, quick-broken crests, slapping,

The strata of color'd clouds, the long bar of maroon-tint away solitary by itself, the spread of purity it lies motionless in,

The horizon's edge, the flying sea-crow, the fragrance of salt marsh and shore mud,

These became part of that child who went forth every day, and who now goes, and will always go forth every day.

I Will Make the True Poem

I will make the true poem of riches,
To earn for the body and the mind whatever adheres and goes
       forward and is not dropt by death;
I will effuse egotism and show it underlying all, and I will be
       the bard of personality,
And I will show of male and female that either is but the equal
       of the other,
And sexual organs and acts! do you concentrate in me, for I
       am determin'd to tell you with courageous clear voice
       to prove you illustrious,
And I will show that there is no imperfection in the present,
       and can be none in the future,
And I will show that whatever happens to anybody it may be
       turn'd to beautiful results,
And I will show that nothing can happen more beautiful than
       death,
And I will thread a thread through my poems that time and
       events are compact,
And that all the things of the universe are perfect miracles,
       each as profound as any.

I will not make poems with reference to parts,
But I will make poems, songs, thoughts, with reference to en-
       semble,
And I will not sing with reference to a day, but with reference
       to all days,
And I will not make a poem nor the least part of a poem but
       has reference to the soul,
Because having look'd at the objects of the universe, I find
       there is no one nor any particle of one but has refer-
       ence to the soul.

Song of Myself

1

I celebrate myself, and sing myself,
And what I assume you shall assume,
For every atom belonging to me as good belongs to you.

I loafe and invite my soul,
I lean and loafe at my ease observing a spear of summer grass.

My tongue, every atom of my blood, form'd from this soil, this
    air,
Born here of parents born here from parents the same, and
    their parents the same,
I, now thirty-seven years old in perfect health begin,
Hoping to cease not till death.

Creeds and schools in abeyance,
Retiring back a while sufficed at what they are, but never for-
    gotten,
I harbor for good or bad, I permit to speak at every hazard,
Nature without check with original energy.

2

Houses and rooms are full of perfumes, the shelves are crowded
    with perfumes,
I breathe the fragrance myself and know it and like it,
The distillation would intoxicate me also, but I shall not let it.

The atmosphere is not a perfume, it has no taste of the distilla-
    tion, it is odorless,
It is for my mouth forever, I am in love with it,
I will go to the bank by the wood and become undisguised and
    naked,
I am mad for it to be in contact with me.

The smoke of my own breath,
Echoes, ripples, buzz'd whispers, love-root, silk-thread, crotch
    and vine,

My respiration and inspiration, the beating of my heart, the
    passing of blood and air through my lungs,
The sniff of green leaves and dry leaves, and of the shore and
    dark-color'd sea-rocks, and of hay in the barn,
The sound of the belch'd words of my voice loos'd to the eddies
    of the wind,
A few light kisses, a few embraces, a reaching around of arms,
The play of shine and shade on the trees as the supple boughs
    wag,
The delight alone or in the rush of the streets, or along the
    fields and hill-sides,
The feeling of health, the full-noon trill, the song of me rising
    from bed and meeting the sun.

Have you reckon'd a thousand acres much? have you reckon'd
    the earth much?
Have you practis'd so long to learn to read?
Have you felt so proud to get at the meaning of poems?

Stop this day and night with me and you shall possess the origin
    of all poems,
You shall possess the good of the earth and sun, (there are
    millions of suns left,)
You shall no longer take things at second or third hand, nor
    look through the eyes of the dead, nor feed on the
    spectres in books,
You shall not look through my eyes either, nor take things from
    me,
You shall listen to all sides and filter them from your self.

3

I have heard what the talkers were talking, the talk of the be-
    ginning and the end,
But I do not talk of the beginning or the end.

There was never any more inception than there is now,
Nor any more youth or age than there is now,

And will never be any more perfection than there is now,
Nor any more heaven or hell than there is now.

Urge and urge and urge,
Always the procreant urge of the world.
Out of the dimness opposite equals advance, always substance
    and increase, always sex,
Always a knit of identity, always distinction, always a breed of
    life.

To elaborate is no avail, learn'd and unlearn'd feel that it is so.

Sure as the most certain sure, plumb in the uprights, well en-
    tretied, braced in the beams,
Stout as a horse, affectionate, haughty, electrical,
I and this mystery here we stand.

Clear and sweet is my soul, and clear and sweet is all that is
    not my soul.

Lack one lacks both, and the unseen is proved by the seen,
Till that becomes unseen and receives proof in its turn.

Showing the best and dividing it from the worst age vexes age,
Knowing the perfect fitness and equanimity of things, while
    they discuss I am silent, and go bathe and admire my-
    self.

Welcome is every organ and attribute of me, and of any man
    hearty and clean,
Not an inch nor a particle of an inch is vile, and none shall be
    less familiar than the rest.

I am satisfied—I see, dance, laugh, sing;
As the hugging and loving bed-fellow sleeps at my side through
    the night, and withdraws at the peep of the day with
    stealthy tread,
Leaving me baskets cover'd with white towels swelling the
    house with their plenty,

Shall I postpone my acceptation and realization and scream at
    my eyes,
That they turn from gazing after and down the road,
And forthwith cipher and show me to a cent,
Exactly the value of one and exactly the value of two, and
    which is ahead?

4

Trippers and askers surround me,
People I meet, the effect upon me of my early life or the ward
    and city I live in, or the nation,
The latest dates, discoveries, inventions, societies, authors old
    and new,
My dinner, dress, associates, looks, compliments, dues,
The real or fancied indifference of some man or woman I love,
The sickness of one of my folks or of myself, or ill-doing or loss
    or lack of money, or depressions or exaltations,
Battles, the horrors of fratricidal war, the fever of doubtful
    news, the fitful events;
These come to me days and nights and go from me again,
But they are not the Me myself.

Apart from the pulling and hauling stands what I am,
Stands amused, complacent, compassionating, idle, unitary,
Looks down, is erect, or bends an arm on an impalpable cer-
    tain rest,
Looking with side-curved head curious what will come next,
Both in and out of the game and watching and wondering at it.

Backward I see in my own days where I sweated through fog
    with linguists and contenders,
I have no mockings or arguments, I witness and wait.

5

I believe in you my soul, the other I am must not abase itself to
    you,
And you must not be abased to the other.

Loafe with me on the grass, loose the stop from your throat,
Not words, not music or rhyme I want, not custom or lecture,
    not even the best,
Only the lull I like, the hum of your valvèd voice.

I mind how once we lay such a transparent summer morning,
How you settled your head athwart my hips and gently turn'd
    over upon me,
And parted the shirt from my bosom-bone, and plunged your
    tongue to my bare-stript heart,
And reach'd till you felt my beard, and reach'd till you held my
    feet.

Swiftly arose and spread around me the peace and knowledge
    that pass all the argument of the earth,
And I know that the hand of God is the promise of my own,
And I know that the spirit of God is the brother of my own,
And that all the men ever born are also my brothers, and the
    women my sisters and lovers,
And that a kelson of the creation is love,
And limitless are leaves stiff or drooping in the fields,
And brown ants in the little wells beneath them,
And mossy scabs of the worm fence, heap'd stones, elder,
    mullein and poke-weed.

6

A child said *What is the grass?* fetching it to me with full hands,
How could I answer the child? I do not know what it is any
    more than he.

I guess it must be the flag of my disposition, out of hopeful
    green stuff woven.

Or I guess it is the handkerchief of the Lord,
A scented gift and remembrancer designedly dropt,
Bearing the owner's name someway in the corners, that we may
    see and remark, and say *Whose?*

Or I guess the grass is itself a child, the produced babe of the
vegetation.

Or I guess it is a uniform hieroglyphic,
And it means, Sprouting alike in broad zones and narrow
zones,
Growing among black folks as among white,
Kanuck, Tuckahoe, Congressman, Cuff, I give them the same,
I receive them the same.

And now it seems to me the beautiful uncut hair of graves.

Tenderly will I use you curling grass,
It may be you transpire from the breasts of young men,
It may be if I had known them I would have loved them,
It may be you are from old people, or from offspring taken
soon out of their mothers' laps,
And here you are the mothers' laps.

This grass is very dark to be from the white heads of old moth-
ers,
Darker than the colorless beards of old men,
Dark to come from under the faint red roofs of mouths.
O I perceive after all so many uttering tongues,
And I perceive they do not come from the roofs of mouths for
nothing.

I wish I could translate the hints about the dead young men
and women,
And the hints about old men and mothers, and the offspring
taken soon out of their laps.

What do you think has become of the young and old men?
And what do you think has become of the women and children?

They are alive and well somewhere,
The smallest sprout shows there is really no death,
And if ever there was it led forward life, and does not wait at
the end to arrest it,
And ceas'd the moment life appear'd.

All goes onward and outward, nothing collapses,
And to die is different from what any one supposed, and
   luckier.

.   .   .   .

Twenty-eight young men bathe by the shore,
Twenty-eight young men and all so friendly;
Twenty-eight years of womanly life and all so lonesome.
She owns the fine house by the rise of the bank,
She hides handsome and richly drest aft the blinds of the win-
   dow.

Which of the young men does she like the best?
Ah the homeliest of them is beautiful to her.

Where are you off to, lady? for I see you,
You splash in the water there, yet stay stock still in your room.

Dancing and laughing along the beach came the twenty-ninth
   bather,
The rest did not see her, but she saw them and loved them.

The beards of the young men glisten'd with wet, it ran from
   their long hair,
Little streams pass'd all over their bodies.

An unseen hand also pass'd over their bodies,
It descended tremblingly from their temples and ribs.

The young men float on their backs, their white bellies bulge to
   the sun, they do not ask who seizes fast to them,
They do not know who puffs and declines with pendant and
   bending arch,
They do not think whom they souse with spray.

.   .   .   .

20

78

Who goes there? hankering, gross, mystical, nude;
How is it I extract strength from the beef I eat?

What is a man anyhow? what am I? what are you?

All I mark as my own you shall offset it with your own,
Else it were time lost listening to me.

I do not snivel that snivel the world over,
That months are vacuums and the ground but wallow and filth.

Whimpering and truckling fold with powders for invalids, conformity goes to the fourth-remov'd,
I wear my hat as I please indoors or out.

Why should I pray? why should I venerate and be ceremo-
nious?

Having pried through the strata, analyzed to a hair, counsel'd
with doctors and calculated close,
I find no sweeter fat than sticks to my own bones.

In all people I see myself, none more and not one a barley-
corn less,
And the good or bad I say of myself I say of them.

I know I am solid and sound,
To me the converging objects of the universe perpetually flow,
All are written to me, and I must get what the writing means.

I know I am deathless,
I know this orbit of mine cannot be swept by a carpenter's
compass,
I know I shall not pass like a child's carlacue cut with a burnt
stick at night.

I know I am august,
I do not trouble my spirit to vindicate itself or be understood,
I see that the elementary laws never apologize,
(I reckon I behave no prouder than the level I plant my house
by, after all.)

I exist as I am, that is enough,
If no other in the world be aware I sit content,
And if each and all be aware I sit content.

One world is aware and by far the largest to me, and that is
        myself,
And whether I come to my own to-day or in ten thousand or
        ten million years,
I can cheerfully take it now, or with equal cheerfulness I can
        wait.
My foothold is tenon'd and mortis'd in granite,
I laugh at what you call dissolution,
And I know the amplitude of time.

.   .   .   .

21

I am the poet of the Body and I am the poet of the Soul,
The pleasures of heaven are with me and the pains of hell are
        with me,
The first I graft and increase upon myself, the latter I trans-
        late into a new tongue.

I am the poet of the woman the same as the man,
And I say it is as great to be a woman as to be a man,
And I say there is nothing greater than the mother of men.

I chant the chant of dilation or pride,
We have had ducking and deprecating about enough,
I show that size is only development.

Have you outstript the rest? are you the President?
It is a trifle, they will more than arrive there every one, and
        still pass on.

I am he that walks with the tender and growing night,
I call to the earth and sea half-held by the night.

Press close bare-bosom'd night—press close magnetic nourish-
        ing night!
Night of south winds—night of the large few stars!
Still nodding night—mad naked summer night.

Smile O voluptuous cool-breath'd earth!
Earth of the slumbering and liquid trees!

Earth of departed sunset—earth of the mountains misty-topt!
Earth of the vitreous pour of the full moon just tinged with
    blue!
Earth of shine and dark mottling the tide of the river!
Earth of the limpid gray of clouds brighter and clearer for my
    sake!
Far-swooping elbow'd earth—rich apple-blossom'd earth!
Smile, for your lover comes.

Prodigal, you have given me love—therefore I to you give
    love!
O unspeakable passionate love.

22

You sea! I resign myself to you also—I guess what you mean,
I behold from the beach your crooked inviting fingers,
I believe you refuse to go back without feeling of me,
We must have a turn together, I undress, hurry me out of
    sight of the land,
Cushion me soft, rock me in billowy drowse,
Dash me with amorous wet, I can repay you.

Sea of stretch'd ground-swells,
Sea breathing broad and convulsive breaths,
Sea of the brine of life and of unshovell'd yet always-ready
    graves,
Howler and scooper of storms, capricious and dainty sea,
I am integral with you, I too am of one phase and of all phases.

Partaker of influx and efflux I, extoller of hate and concilia-
    tion,
Extoller of amies and those that sleep in each others' arms,

I am he attesting sympathy,
(Shall I make my list of things in the house and skip the house
    that supports them?)

I am not the poet of goodness only, I do not decline to be the
    poet of wickedness also.

What blurt is this about virtue and about vice?
Evil propels me and reform of evil propels me, I stand in-
    different,
My gait is no fault-finder's or rejectors gait;
I moisten the roots of all that has grown.

Did you fear some scrofula out of the unflagging pregnancy?
Did you guess the celestial laws are yet to be work'd over and
    rectified?

I find one side a balance and the antipodal side a balance,
Soft doctrine as steady help as stable doctrine,
Thoughts and deeds of the present our rouse and early start.

This minute that comes to me over the past decillions,
There is no better than it and now.

What behaved well in the past or behaves well to-day is not
    such a wonder,
The wonder is always and always how there can be a mean
    man or an infidel.

23

Endless unfolding of words of ages!
And mine a word of the modern, the word En-Masse.

A word of the faith that never balks,
Here or henceforward it is all the same to me, I accept Time
    absolutely.

It alone is without flaw, it alone rounds and completes all,
That mystic baffling wonder alone completes all.

I accept Reality and dare not question it,
Materialism first and last imbuing.

24

Walt Whitman, a kosmos, of Manhattan the son,
Turbulent, fleshy, sensual, eating, drinking and breeding,

No sentimentalist, no stander above men and women or apart
from them,
No more modest than immodest.

Unscrew the locks from the doors!
Unscrew the doors themselves from their jambs!

Whoever degrades another degrades me,
And whatever is done or said returns at last to me.

Through me the afflatus surging and surging, through me the
current and index.

I speak the pass-word primeval, I give the sign of democracy,
By God! I will accept nothing which all cannot have their
counterpart of on the same terms.

Through me many long dumb voices,
Voices of the interminable generations of prisoners and slaves,
Voices of the diseas'd and despairing and of thieves and dwarfs,
Voices of cycles of preparation and accretion,
And of the threads that connect the stars, and of wombs and
of the father-stuff,
And of the rights of them the others are down upon,
Of the deform'd, trivial, flat, foolish, despised,
Fog in the air, beetles rolling balls of dung.

Through me forbidden voices,
Voices of sexes and lusts, voices veil'd and I remove the veil,
Voices indecent by me clarified and transfigur'd.

I do not press my fingers across my mouth,
I keep as delicate around the bowels as around the head and
heart,
Copulation is no more rank to me than death is.

I believe in the flesh and the appetites,
Seeing, hearing, feeling, are miracles, and each part and tag
of me is a miracle.

Divine am I inside and out, and I make holy whatever I touch
or am touch'd from,
The scent of these arm-pits aroma finer than prayer,
This head more than churches, bibles, and all the creeds.

If I worship one thing more than another it shall be the spread
of my own body, or any part of it,
Translucent mould of me it shall be you!
Shaded ledges and rests it shall be you!
Firm masculine colter it shall be you!
Whatever goes to the tilth of me it shall be you!
You my rich blood! your milky stream pale strippings of my
life!
Breast that presses against other breasts it shall be you!
My brain it shall be your occult convolutions!
Root of wash'd sweet-flag! timorous pond-snipe! nest of guarded
duplicate eggs! it shall be you!
Mix'd tussled hay of head, beard, brawn, it shall be you!
Trickling sap of maple, fibre of manly wheat, it shall be you!
Sun so generous it shall be you!
Vapors lighting and shading my face it shall be you!
You sweaty brooks and dews it shall be you!
Winds whose soft-tickling genitals rub against me it shall be
you!
Broad muscular fields, branches of live oak, loving lounger in
my winding paths, it shall be you!
Hands I have taken, face I have kiss'd, mortal I have ever
touch'd, it shall be you.

I dote on myself, there is that lot of me and all so luscious,
Each moment and whatever happens thrills me with joy,
I cannot tell how my ankles bend, nor whence the cause of my
faintest wish,
Nor the cause of the friendship I emit, nor the cause of the
84   friendship I take again.

That I walk up my stoop, I pause to consider if it really be,

A morning-glory at my window satisfies me more than the meta-
      physics of books.

To behold the day-break!
The little light fades the immense and diaphanous shadows,
The air tastes good to my palate.

Hefts of the moving world at innocent gambols silently rising,
      freshly exuding,
Scooting obliquely high and low.

Something I cannot see puts upward libidinous prongs,
Seas of bright juice suffuse heaven.

The earth by the sky staid with, the daily close of their junc-
      tion,
The heav'd challenge from the east that moment over my head,
The mocking taunt, See then whether you shall be master!

25

Dazzling and tremendous how quick the sun-rise would kill me,
If I could not now and always send sun-rise out of me.

We also ascend dazzling and tremendous as the sun,
We found our own O my soul in the calm and cool of the day-
      break.

My voice goes after what my eyes cannot reach,
With the twirl of my tongue I encompass worlds and volumes
      of worlds.

Speech is the twin of my vision, it is unequal to measure itself,
It provokes me forever, it says sarcastically,
Walt you contain enough, why don't you let it out then?

Come now I will not be tantalized, you conceive too much of
      articulation,
Do you not know O speech how the buds beneath you are
      folded?

Waiting in gloom, protected by frost,
The dirt receding before my prophetical screams,
I underlying causes to balance them at last,
My knowledge my live parts, it keeping tally with the meaning
of all things,
Happiness, (which whoever hears me let him or her set out in
search of this day.)

My final merit I refuse you, I refuse putting from me what I
really am,
Encompass worlds, but never try to encompass me,
I crowd your sleekest and best by simply looking toward you.

Writing and talk do not prove me,
I carry the plenum of proof and every thing else in my face,
With the hush of my lips I wholly confound the skeptic.

.   .   .   .

31

I believe a leaf of grass is no less than the journey-work of the
stars,
And the pismire is equally perfect, and a grain of sand, and the
egg of the wren,
And the tree-toad is a chef-d'œuvre for the highest,
And the running blackberry would adorn the parlors of heaven,
And the narrowest hinge in my hand puts to scorn all ma-
chinery,
And the cow crunching with depress'd head surpasses any
statue,
And a mouse is miracle enough to stagger sextillions of in-
fidels.

I find I incorporate gneiss, coal, long-threaded moss, fruits,
grains, esculent roots,
And am stucco'd with quadrupeds and birds all over,
And have distanced what is behind me for good reasons,
But call any thing back again when I desire it.

In vain the speeding or shyness,
In vain the plutonic rocks send their old heat against my approach,
In vain the mastodon retreats beneath its own powder'd bones,
In vain objects stand leagues off and assume manifold shapes,
In vain the ocean settling in hollows and the great monsters lying low,
In vain the buzzard houses herself with the sky,
In vain the snake slides through the creepers and logs,
In vain the elk takes to the inner passes of the woods,
In vain the razor-bill'd auk sails far north to Labrador,
I follow quickly, I ascend to the nest in the fissure of the cliff.

32

I think I could turn and live with animals, they are so placid and self-contain'd,
I stand and look at them long and long.

They do not sweat and whine about their condition,
They do not lie awake in the dark and weep for their sins,
They do not make me sick discussing their duty to God,
Not one is dissatisfied, not one is demented with the mania of owning things,
Not one kneels to another, nor to his kind that lived thousands of years ago,
Not one is respectable or unhappy over the whole earth.
So they show their relations to me and I accept them,
They bring me tokens of myself, they evince them plainly in their possession.

I wonder where they get those tokens,
Did I pass that way huge times ago and negligently drop them?

Myself moving forward then and now and forever,
Gathering and showing more always and with velocity,
Infinite and omnigenous, and the like of these among them,
Not too exclusive toward the reachers of my remembrancers,

Picking out here one that I love, and now go with him on
brotherly terms.

A gigantic beauty of a stallion, fresh and responsive to my
caresses,
Head high in the forehead, wide between the ears,
Limbs glossy and supple, tail dusting the ground,
Eyes full of sparkling wickedness, ears finely cut, flexibly
moving.

His nostrils dilate as my heels embrace him,
His well-built limbs tremble with pleasure as we race around
and return.
I but use you a minute, then I resign you, stallion,
Why do I need your paces when I myself out-gallop them?
Even as I stand or sit passing faster than you.

.   .   .   .

35

Would you hear of an old-time sea-fight?
Would you learn who won by the light of the moon and stars?
List to the yarn, as my grandmother's father the sailor told it
to me.

Our foe was no skulk in his ship I tell you, (said he,)
His was the surly English pluck, and there is no tougher or
truer, and never was, and never will be;
Along the lower'd eve he came horribly raking us.

We closed with him, the yards entangled, the cannon touch'd,
My captain lash'd fast with his own hands.

We had receiv'd some eighteen pound shots under the water,
On our lower-gun-deck two large pieces had burst at the first
fire, killing all around and blowing up overhead.

88 Fighting at sun-down, fighting at dark,
Ten o'clock at night, the full moon well up, our leaks on the
gain, and five feet of water reported,

The master-at-arms loosing the prisoners confined in the after-
hold to give them a chance for themselves.

The transit to and from the magazine is now stopt by the sen-
tinels,
They see so many strange faces they do not know whom to trust.

Our frigate takes fire,
The other asks if we demand quarter?
If our colors are struck and the fighting done?

Now I laugh content, for I hear the voice of my little captain,
We have not struck, he composedly cries, *we have just begun
our part of the fighting.*

Only three guns are in use,
One is directed by the captain himself against the enemy's
main-mast,
Two well serv'd with grape and canister silence his musketry
and clear his decks.

The tops alone second the fire of this little battery, especially
the main-top,
They hold out bravely during the whole of the action.

Not a moment's cease,
The leaks gain fast on the pumps, the fire eats toward the
powder-magazine.

One of the pumps has been shot away, it is generally thought
we are sinking.

Serene stands the little captain,
He is not hurried, his voice is neither high nor low,
His eyes give more light to us than our battle-lanterns.

89

Toward twelve there in the beams of the moon they surrender
to us.

36

Stretch'd and still lies the midnight,
Two great hulls motionless on the breast of the darkness,
Our vessel riddled and slowly sinking, preparations to pass to
    the one we have conquer'd,
The captain on the quarter-deck coldly giving his orders
    through a countenance white as a sheet,
Near by the corpse of the child that serv'd in the cabin,
The dead face of an old salt with long white hair and carefully
    curl'd whiskers,
The flames spite of all that can be done flickering aloft and
    below,
The husky voices of the two or three officers yet fit for duty,
Formless stacks of bodies and bodies by themselves, dabs of
    flesh upon the masts and spars,
Cut of cordage, dangle of rigging, slight shock of the soothe of
    waves,
Black and impassive guns, litter of powder-parcels, strong scent,
A few large stars overhead, silent and mournful shining,
Delicate sniffs of sea-breeze, smells of sedgy grass and fields by
    the shore, death-messages given in charge to survivors,
The hiss of the surgeon's knife, the gnawing teeth of his saw,
Wheeze, cluck, swash of falling blood, short wild scream, and
    long, dull, tapering groan,
These so, these irretrievable.

37

You laggards there on guard! look to your arms!
In at the conquer'd doors they crowd! I am possess'd!
Embody all presences outlaw'd or suffering,
See myself in prison shaped like another man.
And feel the dull unintermitted pain,
For me the keepers of convicts shoulder their carbines and
    keep watch.
90   It is I let out in the morning and barr'd at night.

Not a mutineer walks handcuff'd to jail but I am handcuff'd to
    him and walk by his side,

(I am less the jolly one there, and more the silent one with
    sweat on my twitching lips.)

Not a youngster is taken for larceny but I go up too, and am
    tried and sentenced.

Not a cholera patient lies at the last gasp but I also lie at the
    last gasp,
My face is ash-color'd, my sinews gnarl, away from me people
    retreat.

Askers embody themselves in me and I am embodied in them,
I project my hat, sit shame-faced, and beg.

. . . .

40

Flaunt of the sunshine I need not your bask—lie over!
You light surfaces only, I force surfaces and depths also.

Earth! you seem to look for something at my hands,
Say, old top-knot, what do you want?

Man or woman, I might tell how I like you, but cannot,
And might tell what it is in me and what it is in you, but
    cannot,
And might tell that pining I have, that pulse of my nights and
    days.

Behold, I do not give lectures or a little charity,
When I give I give myself.

You there, impotent, loose in the knees,
Open your scarf'd chops till I blow grit within you,
Spread your palms and lift the flaps of your pockets,
I am not to be denied, I compel, I have stores plenty and to
    spare,
And any thing I have I bestow.

I do not ask who you are, that is not important to me,
You can do nothing and be nothing but what I will infold you.

91

To cotton-field drudge or cleaner of privies I lean,
On his right cheek I put the family kiss,
And in my soul I swear I never will deny him.

On women fit for conception I start bigger and nimbler babes,
(This day I am jetting the stuff of far more arrogant republics.)

To any one dying, thither I speed and twist the knob of the door,
Turn the bed-clothes toward the foot of the bed,
Let the physician and the priest go home.

I seize the descending man and raise him with resistless will,
O despairer, here is my neck,
By God, you shall not go down! hang your whole weight upon
    me.

I dilate you with tremendous breath, I buoy you up,
Every room of the house do I fill with an arm'd force,
Lovers of me, bafflers of graves.

Sleep—I and they keep guard all night,
Not doubt, not disease shall dare to lay finger upon you,
I have embraced you, and henceforth possess you to myself,
And when you rise in the morning you will find what I tell you
    is so.

.   .   .   .

44

It is time to explain myself—let us stand up.

What is known I strip away,
I launch all men and women forward with me into the Un-
    known.
The clock indicates the moment—but what does eternity indi-
    cate?

We have thus far exhausted trillions of winters and summers,
There are trillions ahead, and trillions ahead of them.

Births have brought us richness and variety,
And other births will bring us richness and variety.

I do not call one greater and one smaller,
That which fills its period and place is equal to any.

Were mankind murderous or jealous upon you, my brother,
        my sister?
I am sorry for you, they are not murderous or jealous upon me,
All has been gentle with me, I keep no account with lamenta-
        tion,
(What have I to do with lamentation?)

I am an acme of things accomplish'd, and I an encloser of
        things to be.

My feet strike an apex of the apices of the stairs,
On every step bunches of ages, and larger bunches between
        the steps,
All below duly travel'd, and still I mount and mount.

Rise after rise bow the phantoms behind me,
Afar down I see the huge first Nothing, I know I was even there,
I waited unseen and always, and slept through the lethargic
        mist,
And took my time, and took no hurt from the fetid carbon.

Long I was hugg'd close—long and long.

Immense have been the preparations for me,
Faithful and friendly the arms that have help'd me.

Cycles ferried my cradle, rowing and rowing like cheerful
        boatmen,
For room to me stars kept aside in their own rings,
They sent influences to look after what was to hold me.

Before I was born out of my mother generations guided me,
My embryo has never been torpid, nothing could overlay it.

For it the nebula cohered to an orb,
The long slow strata piled to rest it on,
Vast vegetables gave it sustenance,

Monstrous sauroids transported it in their mouths and deposited it with care.

All forces have been steadily employ'd to complete and delight
me,
Now on this spot I stand with my robust soul.

. . . .

46

I know I have the best of time and space, and was never measured and never will be measured.

I tramp a perpetual journey, (come listen all!)
My signs are a rain-proof coat, good shoes, and a staff cut from
the woods,
No friend of mine takes his ease in my chair,
I have no chair, no church, no philosophy,
I lead no man to a dinner-table, library, exchange,
But each man and each woman of you I lead upon a knoll,
My left hand hooking you round the waist,
My right hand pointing to landscapes of continents and the
public road.

Not I, not any one else can travel that road for you,
You must travel it for yourself.

It is not far, it is within reach,
Perhaps you have been on it since you were born and did not
know,
Perhaps it is everywhere on water and on land.

Shoulder your duds dear son, and I will mine, and let us hasten
forth,
Wonderful cities and free nations we shall fetch as we go.

If you tire, give me both burdens, and rest the chuff of your
hand on my hip,
And in due time you shall repay the same service to me,
For after we start we never lie by again.

This day before dawn I ascended a hill and look'd at the
    crowded heaven,
And I said to my spirit *When we become the enfolders of those*
    orbs, and the pleasure and knowledge of every thing in
    them, shall we be fill'd and satisfied then?
And my spirit said *No, we but level that lift to pass and con-*
    tinue beyond.

You are also asking me questions and I hear you,
I answer that I cannot answer, you must find out for yourself.

Sit a while dear son,
Here are biscuits to eat and here is milk to drink,
But as soon as you sleep and renew yourself in sweet clothes, I
    kiss you with a good-by kiss and open the gate for your
    egress hence.

Long enough have you dream'd contemptible dreams,
Now I wash the gum from your eyes,
You must habit yourself to the dazzle of the light and of every
    moment of your life.

Long have you timidly waded holding a plank by the shore,
Now I will you to be a bold swimmer,
To jump off in the midst of the sea, rise again, nod to me, shout,
    and laughingly dash with your hair.

47

I am the teacher of athletes,
He that by me spreads a wider breast than my own proves the
    width of my own,
He most honors my style who learns under it to destroy the
    teacher.

The boy I love, the same becomes a man not through derived
    power, but in his own right,
Wicked rather than virtuous out of conformity or fear,
Fond of his sweetheart, relishing well his steak,
Unrequited love or a slight cutting him worse than sharp steel
    cuts,

First-rate to ride, to fight, to hit the bull's eye, to sail a skiff, to
 sing a song or play on the banjo,
Preferring scars and the beard and faces pitted with smallpox
 over all latherers,
And those well-tann'd to those that keep out of the sun.

I teach straying from me, yet who can stray from me?
I follow you whoever you are from the present hour,
My words itch at your ears till you understand them.

I do not say these things for a dollar or to fill up the time while
 I wait for a boat,
(It is you talking just as much as myself, I act as the tongue of
 you,
Tied in your mouth, in mine it begins to be loosen'd.)

I swear I will never again mention love or death inside a house,
And I swear I will never translate myself at all, only to him or
 her who privately stays with me in the open air.

If you would understand me go to the heights or water-shore,
The nearest gnat is an explanation, and a drop or motion of
 waves a key,
The maul, the oar, the hand-saw, second my words.

No shutter'd room or school can commune with me,
But roughs and little children better than they.

The young mechanic is closest to me, he knows me well,
The woodman that takes his axe and·jug with him shall take me
 with him all day,
The farm-boy ploughing in the field feels good at the sound of
 my voice,
In vessels that sail my words sail, I go with fishermen and seamen and love them.

The soldier camp'd or upon the march is mine,
On the night ere the pending battle many seek me, and I do
 not fail them,

On that solemn night (it may be their last) those that know
    me seek me.

My face rubs to the hunter's face when he lies down alone in
    his blanket,
The driver thinking of me does not mind the jolt of his wagon,
The young mother and old mother comprehend me,
The girl and the wife rest the needle a moment and forget
    where they are,
They and all would resume what I have told them.

48

I have said that the soul is not more than the body,
And I have said that the body is not more than the soul,
And nothing, not God, is greater to one than one's self is,
And whoever walks a furlong without sympathy walks to his
    own funeral drest in his shroud,
And I or you pocketless of a dime may purchase the pick of
    the earth,
And to glance with an eye or show a bean in its pod confounds
    the learning of all times,
And there is no trade or employment but the young man fol-
    lowing it may become a hero,
And there is no object so soft but it makes a hub for the wheel'd
    universe,
And I say to any man or woman, Let your soul stand cool and
    composed before a million universes.

And I say to mankind, Be not curious about God,
For I who am curious about each am not curious about God.
(No array of terms can say how much I am at peace about
    God and about death.)

I hear and behold God in every object, yet understand God not
    in the least,
Nor do I understand who there can be more wonderful than
    myself.

Why should I wish to see God better than this day?

I see something of God each hour of the twenty-four, and each
moment then,
In the faces of men and women I see God, and in my own face
in the glass,
I find letters from God dropt in the street, and every one is
sign'd by God's name,
And I leave them where they are, for I know that wheresoe'er
I go
Others will punctually come for ever and ever.

49

And as to you Death, and you bitter hug of mortality, it is idle
to try to alarm me.

To his work without flinching the accoucheur comes,
I see the elder-hand pressing receiving supporting,
I recline by the sills of the exquisite flexible doors,
And mark the outlet, and mark the relief and escape.

And as to you Corpse I think you are good manure, but that
does not offend me,
I smell the white roses sweet-scented and growing.
I reach to the leafy lips, I reach to the polish'd breasts of
melons.

And as to you Life I reckon you are the leavings of many
deaths,
(No doubt I have died myself ten thousand times before.)

I hear you whispering there O stars of heaven,
O suns—O grass of graves—O perpetual transfers and promo-
tions,
If you do not say any thing how can I say any thing?

Of the turbid pool that lies in the autumn forest,
Of the moon that descends the steeps of the soughing twilight,
Toss, sparkles of day and dusk—toss on the black stems that
decay in the muck,
Toss to the moaning gibberish of the dry limbs.

I ascend from the moon, I ascend from the night,
I perceive that the ghastly glimmer is noonday sunbeams re-
flected,
And debouch to the steady and central from the offspring great
or small.

50

There is that in me—I do not know what it is—but I know it
is in me.

Wrench'd and sweaty—calm and cool then my body becomes,
I sleep—I sleep long.

I do not know it—it is without name—it is a word unsaid,
It is not in any dictionary, utterance, symbol.

Something it swings on more than the earth I swing on,
To it the creation is the friend whose embracing awakes me.

Perhaps I might tell more. Outlines! I plead for my brothers
and sisters.

Do you see O my brothers and sisters?
It is not chaos or death—it is form, union, plan—it is eternal
life—it is Happiness.

51

The past and present wilt—I have fill'd them, emptied them,
And proceed to fill my next fold of the future.

Listener up there! what have you to confide to me?
Look in my face while I snuff the sidle of evening,
(Talk honestly, no one else hears you, and I stay only a minute
longer.)

Do I contradict myself?
Very well then I contradict myself,
(I am large, I contain multitudes.)

I concentrate toward them that are nigh, I wait on the door-
slab.

Who has done his day's work? who will soonest be through
with his supper?
Who wishes to walk with me?

Will you speak before I am gone? will you prove already too
late?

52

The spotted hawk swoops by and accuses me, he complains of
my gab and my loitering.

I too am not a bit tamed, I too am untranslatable,
I sound my barbaric yawp over the roofs of the world.

The last scud of day holds back for me,
It flings my likeness after the rest and true as any on the shad-
ow'd wilds,
It coaxes me to the vapor and the dusk.

I depart as air, I shake my white locks at the runaway sun,
I effuse my flesh in eddies, and drift it in lacy jags.

I bequeath myself to the dirt to grow from the grass I love,
If you want me again look for me under your boot-soles.

You will hardly know who I am or what I mean,
But I shall be good health to you nevertheless,
And filter and fibre your blood.

Failing to fetch me at first keep encouraged,
Missing me one place search another,
I stop somewhere waiting for you.

Whoever You Are Holding Me Now in Hand

Whoever you are holding me now in hand,
Without one thing all will be useless,
I give you fair warning before you attempt me further,
I am not what you supposed, but far different.

Who is he that would become my follower?
Who would sign himself a candidate for my affections?

The way is suspicious, the result uncertain, perhaps destructive,
You would have to give up all else, I alone would expect to be
        your sole and exclusive standard,
Your novitiate would even then be long and exhausting,
The whole past theory of your life and all conformity to the
        lives around you would have to be abandon'd,
Therefore release me now before troubling yourself any fur-
        ther, let go your hand from my shoulders,
Put me down and depart on your way.

Or else by stealth in some wood for trial,
Or back of a rock in the open air,
(For in any roof'd room of a house I emerge not, nor in com-
        pany,
And in libraries I lie as one dumb, a gawk, or unborn, or
        dead,)
But just possibly with you on a high hill, first watching lest any
        person for miles around approach unawares,

Or possibly with you sailing at sea, or on the beach of the sea
or some quiet island,
Here to put your lips upon mine I permit you,
With the comrade's long-dwelling kiss or the new husband's
kiss,
For I am the new husband and I am the comrade.

Or if you will, thrusting me beneath your clothing,
Where I may feel the throbs of your heart or rest upon your
hip,
Carry me when you go forth over land or sea;
For thus merely touching you is enough, is best,
And thus touching you would I silently sleep and be carried
eternally.

But these leaves conning you con at peril,
For these leaves and me you will not understand,
They will elude you at first and still more afterward, I will cer-
tainly elude you,
Even while you should think you had unquestionably caught
me, behold!
Already you see I have escaped from you.

For it is not for what I have put into it that I have written this
book,
Nor is it by reading it you will acquire it,
Nor do those know me best who admire me and vauntingly
praise me,
Nor will the candidates for my love (unless at most a very few)
prove victorious,
Nor will my poems do good only, they will do just as much evil,
perhaps more,
For all is useless without that which you may guess at many
times and not hit, that which I hinted at;
Therefore release me and depart on your way.

When I Read the Book

When I read the book, the biography famous,
And is this then (said I) what the author calls a man's life?
And so will some one when I am dead and gone write my life?
(As if any man really knew aught of my life,
Why even I myself I often think know little or nothing of my
      real life,
Only a few hints, a few diffused faint clews and indirections
I seek for my own use to trace out here.)

When I Heard the Learn'd Astronomer

When I heard the learn'd astronomer,
When the proofs, the figures, were ranged in columns before
      me,
When I was shown the charts and diagrams, to add, divide, and
      measure them,
When I sitting heard the astronomer where he lectured with
      much applause in the lecture-room,
How soon unaccountable I became tired and sick,
Till rising and gliding out I wander'd off by myself,
In the mystical moist night-air, and from time to time,
Look'd up in perfect silence at the stars.

I Sit and Look Out

I sit and look out upon all the sorrows of the world, and upon
      all oppression and shame,
I hear secret convulsive sobs from young men at anguish with
      themselves, remorseful after deeds done,
I see in low life the mother misused by her children, dying,
      neglected, gaunt, desperate,
I see the wife misused by her husband, I see the treacherous
      seducer of young women,
I mark the ranklings of jealousy and unrequited love attempted
      to be hid, I see these sights on the earth,
I see the workings of battle, pestilence, tyranny, I see martyrs
      and prisoners,
I observe a famine at sea, I observe the sailors casting lots who
      shall be kill'd to preserve the lives of the rest,
I observe the slights and degradations cast by arrogant persons
      upon laborers, the poor, and upon Negroes, and the
      like;
All these—all the meanness and agony without end I sitting
      look out upon,
See, hear, and am silent.

Shut Not Your Doors

Shut not your doors to me proud libraries,
For that which was lacking on all your well-fill'd shelves, yet
        needed most, I bring,
Forth from the war emerging, a book I have made,
The words of my book nothing, the drift of it every thing,
A book separate, not link'd with the rest nor felt by the intel-
        lect,
But you ye untold latencies will thrill to every page.

Hast Never Come to Thee an Hour

Hast never come to thee an hour,
A sudden gleam divine, precipitating, bursting all these bub-
        bles, fashions, wealth?
These eager business aims—books, politics, art, amours,
To utter nothingness?

LOVE POEMS

To a Stranger

Passing stranger! you do not know how longingly I look upon
    you,
You must be he I was seeking, or she I was seeking, (it comes
    to me as of a dream,)
I have somewhere surely lived a life of joy with you,
All is recall'd as we flit by each other, fluid, affectionate, chaste,
    matured,
You grew up with me, were a boy with me or a girl with me,
I ate with you and slept with you, your body has become not
    yours only nor left my body mine only,
You give me the pleasure of your eyes, face, flesh, as we pass,
    you take of my beard, breast, hands, in return,
I am not to speak to you, I am to think of you when I sit alone
    or wake at night alone,
I am to wait, I do not doubt I am to meet you again,
I am to see to it that I do not lose you.

As Adam Early in the Morning

As Adam early in the morning,
Walking forth from the bower refresh'd with sleep,
Behold me where I pass, hear my voice, approach,
Touch me, touch the palm of your hand to my body as I pass,
Be not afraid of my body.

I Am He That Aches with Love

I am he that aches with amorous love;
Does the earth gravitate; does not all matter, aching, attract all
      matter?
So the body of me to all I meet or know.

Out of the Rolling Ocean the Crowd

Out of the rolling ocean the crowd came a drop gently to me,
Whispering *I love you, before long I die,*
I have travel'd a long way merely to look on you to touch you,
For I could not die till I once look'd on you,
For I fear'd I might afterward lose you.

Now we have met, we have look'd, we are safe,
Return in peace to the ocean my love,
I too am part of that ocean my love, we are not so much
      separated,
Behold the great rondure, the cohesion of all, how perfect!
But as for me, for you, the irresistible sea is to separate us,
As for an hour carrying us diverse, yet cannot carry us diverse
      forever;
Be not impatient—a little space—know you I salute the air,
      the ocean and the land,
Every day at sundown for your dear sake my love.

109

Are You the New Person Drawn Toward Me?

Are you the new person drawn toward me?
To begin with take warning, I am surely far different from
what you suppose;
Do you suppose you will find in me your ideal?
Do you think it is so easy to have me become your lover?
Do you think the friendship of me would be unalloy'd satisfac-
tion?
Do you think I am trusty and faithful?
Do you see no further than this façade, this smooth and tolerant
manner of me?
Do you suppose yourself advancing on real ground toward a
real heroic man?
Have you no thought O dreamer that it may be all maya, illu-
sion?

O Hymen! O Hymenee!

O hymen! O hymenee! why do you tantalize me thus?
O why sting me for a swift moment only?
Why can you not continue? O why do you now cease?
Is it because if you continued beyond the swift moment you
would soon certainly kill me?

Once I Pass'd Through a Populous City

Once I pass'd through a populous city imprinting my brain for
      future use with its shows, architecture, customs, tradi-
      tions,
Yet now of all that city I remember only a woman I casually
      met there who detain'd me for love of me,
Day by day and night by night we were together—all else has
      long been forgotten by me,
I remember I say only that woman who passionately clung to
      me,
Again we wander, we love, we separate again,
Again she holds me by the hand, I must not go,
I see her close beside me with silent lips sad and tremulous.

To a Common Prostitute

Be composed—be at ease with me—I am Walt Whitman, lib-
      eral and lusty as Nature,
Not till the sun excludes you do I exclude you,
Not till the waters refuse to glisten for you and the leaves to
      rustle for you, do my words refuse to glisten and rustle
      for you.

My girl I appoint with you an appointment, and I charge you
      that you make preparations to be worthy to meet me,
And I charge you that you be patient and perfect till I come.

Till then I salute you with a significant look that you do not
      forget me.

111

I Sing the Body Electric

1

I sing the body electric,
The armies of those I love engirth me and I engirth them,
They will not let me off till I go with them, respond to them,
And discorrupt them, and charge them full with the charge of
     the soul.

Was it doubted that those who corrupt their own bodies con-
     ceal themselves?
And if those who defile the living are as bad as they who defile
     the dead?
And if the body does not do fully as much as the soul?
And if the body were not the soul, what is the soul?

.   .   .   .

2

The love of the body of man or woman balks account, the body
     itself balks account,
That of the male is perfect, and that of the female is perfect.

The expression of the face balks account,
But the expression of a well-made man appears not only in his
     face,
It is in his limbs and joints also, it is curiously in the joints of
     his hips and wrists,
It is in his walk, the carriage of his neck, the flex of his waist
     and knees, dress does not hide him,
The strong sweet quality he has strikes through the cotton and
     broadcloth,
To see him pass conveys as much as the best poem, perhaps
     more,
You linger to see his back, and the back of his neck and shoul-
     der-side.

The sprawl and fulness of babes, the bosoms and heads of
women, the folds of their dress, their style as we pass in
the street, the contour of their shape downwards,
The swimmer naked in the swimming-bath, seen as he swims
through the transparent green-shine, or lies with his
face up and rolls silently to and fro in the heave of the
water,
The bending forward and backward of rowers in row-boats,
the horseman in his saddle,
Girls, mothers, house-keepers, in all their performances,
The group of laborers seated at noon-time with their open dinner kettles, and their wives waiting,
The female soothing a child, the farmer's daughter in the garden or cow-yard,
The young fellow hoeing corn, the sleigh-driver driving his six
horses through the crowd,
The wrestle of wrestlers, two apprentice-boys, quite grown,
lusty, good-natured, native-born, out on the vacant lot
at sundown after work,
The coats and caps thrown down, the embrace of love and re-
sistance,
The upper-hold and under-hold, the hair rumpled over and
blinding the eyes;
The march of firemen in their own costumes, the play of masculine muscle through clean-setting trowsers and waist-
straps,
The slow return from the fire, the pause when the bell strikes
suddenly again, and the listening on the alert,
The natural, perfect, varied attitudes, the bent head, the curv'd
neck and the counting;
Such-like I love—I loosen myself, pass freely, am at the mother's breast with the little child,
Swim with the swimmers, wrestle with wrestlers, march in line
with the firemen, and pause, listen, count.

. . . .   **113**

O my body! I dare not desert the likes of you in other men and
women, nor the likes of the parts of you,
I believe the likes of you are to stand or fall with the likes of
the soul, (and that they are the soul,)
I believe the likes of you shall stand or fall with my poems, and
that they are my poems,
Man's, woman's, child's, youth's, wife's, husband's, mother's,
father's, young man's, young woman's poems,
Head, neck, hair, ears, drop and tympan of the ears,
Eyes, eye-fringes, iris of the eye, eyebrows, and the waking or
sleeping of the lids,
Mouth, tongue, lips, teeth, roof of the mouth, jaws, and the jaw-
hinges,
Nose, nostrils of the nose, and the partition,
Cheeks, temples, forehead, chin, throat, back of the neck, neck-
slue,
Strong shoulders, manly beard, scapula, hind-shoulders, and
the ample side-round of the chest,
Upper-arm, armpit, elbow-socket, lower-arm, arm-sinews, arm-
bones,
Wrist and wrist-joints, hand, palm, knuckles, thumb, fore-
finger, finger-joints, finger-nails,
Broad breast-front, curling hair of the breast, breast-bone,
breast-side,
Ribs, belly, backbone, joints of the backbone,
Hips, hip-sockets, hip-strength, inward and outward round,
man-balls, man-root,
Strong set of thighs, well carrying the trunk above,
Leg-fibres, knee, knee-pan, upper-leg, under-leg,
Ankles, instep, foot-ball, toes, toe-joints, the heel;
All attitudes, all the shapeliness, all the belongings of my or
your body or of any one's body, male or female,
The lung-sponges, the stomach-sac, the bowels sweet and clean,
The brain in its folds inside the skull-frame,
Sympathies, heart-valves, palate-valves, sexuality, maternity,

114

Womanhood and all that is a woman, and the man that comes
     from woman,
The womb, the teats, nipples, breast-milk, tears, laughter,
     weeping, love-looks, love-perturbations and risings,
The voice, articulation, language, whispering, shouting aloud,
Food, drink, pulse, digestion, sweat, sleep, walking, swimming,
Poise on the hips, leaping, reclining, embracing, arm-curving
     and tightening,
The continual changes of the flex of the mouth, and around the
     eyes,
The skin, the sunburnt shade, freckles, hair,
The curious sympathy one feels when feeling with the hand the
     naked meat of the body,
The circling rivers the breath, and breathing it in and out,
The beauty of the waist, and thence of the hips, and thence
     downward toward the knees,
The thin red jellies within you or within me, the bones and the
     marrow in the bones,
The exquisite realization of health;
O I say these are not the parts and poems of the body only, but
     of the soul,
O I say now these are the soul!

We Two, How Long We Were Fool'd

We two, how long we were fool'd,
Now transmuted, we swiftly escape as Nature escapes,
We are Nature, long have we been absent, but now we return,
We become plants, trunks, foliage, roots, bark,
We are bedded in the ground, we are rocks,
We are oaks, we grow in the openings side by side,
We browse, we are two among the wild herds spontaneous as
        any,
We are two fishes swimming in the sea together,
We are what locust blossoms are, we drop scent around lanes
        mornings and evenings,
We are also the coarse smut of beasts, vegetables, minerals,
We are two predatory hawks, we soar above and look down,
We are two resplendent suns, we it is who balance ourselves
        orbic and stellar, we are as two comets,
We prowl fang'd and four-footed in the woods, we spring on
        prey,
We are two clouds forenoons and afternoons driving overhead,
We are seas mingling, we are two of those cheerful waves roll-
        ing over each other and interwetting each other,
We are what the atmosphere is, transparent, receptive, per-
        vious, impervious,
We are snow, rain, cold, darkness, we are each product and
        influence of the globe,
We have circled and circled till we have arrived home again,
        we too,
We have voided all but freedom and all but our own joy.

I Hear It Was Charged Against Me

I hear it was charged against me that I sought to destroy insti-
      tutions,
But really I am neither for nor against institutions,
(What indeed have I in common with them? or what with the
      destruction of them?)
Only I will establish in the Mannahatta and in every city of
      these States inland and seaboard,
And in the fields and woods, and above every keel little or
      large that dents the water,
Without edifices or rules or trustees or any argument,
The institution of the dear love of comrades.

WAR POEMS

Beat! Beat! Drums!

Beat! beat! drums—blow! bugles, blow!
Through the windows—through doors—burst like a ruthless
        force,
Into the solemn church, and scatter the congregation,
Into the school where the scholar is studying;
Leave not the bridegroom quiet—no happiness must he have
        now with his bride,
Nor the peaceful farmer any peace, ploughing his field or
        gathering his grain,
So fierce you whirr and pound you drums—so shrill you bugles
        blow.

Beat! beat! drums—blow! bugles! blow!
Over the traffic of cities—over the rumble of wheels in the
        streets;
Are beds prepared for sleepers at night in the houses? no
        sleepers must sleep in those beds,
No bargainers' bargains by day—no brokers or speculators—
        would they continue?
Would the talkers be talking? would the singer attempt to sing?
Would the lawyer rise in the court to state his case before the
        judge?
Then rattle quicker, heavier drums—you bugles wilder blow.

Beat! beat! drums!—blow! bugles! blow!
Make no parley—stop for no expostulation,
Mind not the timid—mind not the weeper or prayer,
Mind not the old man beseeching the young man,
Let not the child's voice be heard, nor the mother's entreaties,
Make even the trestles to shake the dead where they lie await-
        ing the hearses,
So strong you thump O terrible drums—so loud you bugles
        blow.

Bivouac on a Mountain Side

I see before me now a traveling army halting,
Below a fertile valley spread, with barns and the orchards of
summer,
Behind, the terraced sides of a mountain, abrupt, in places
rising high,
Broken, with rocks, with clinging cedars, with tall shapes
dingily seen,
The numerous camp-fires scatter'd near and far, some away
up on the mountain,
The shadowy forms of men and horses, looming, large-sized,
flickering,
And over all the sky—the sky! far, far out of reach, studded,
breaking out, the eternal stars.

By the Bivouac's Fitful Flame

By the bivouac's fitful flame,
A procession winding around me, solemn and sweet and slow
—but first I note,
The tents of the sleeping army, the fields' and woods' dim out-
line,
The darkness lit by spots of kindled fire, the silence,
Like a phantom far or near an occasional figure moving,
The shrubs and trees, (as I lift my eyes they seem to be stealth-
ily watching me,)
While wind in procession thoughts, O tender and wondrous
thoughts,
Of life and death, of home and the past and loved, and of those
that are far away;
A solemn and slow procession there as I sit on the ground,
By the bivouac's fitful flame.

121

Year of Meteors

(1859-60)

Year of meteors! brooding year!
I would bind in words retrospective some of your deeds and
    signs,
I would sing your contest for the 19th Presidentiad,
I would sing how an old man, tall, with white hair, mounted the
    scaffold in Virginia,
(I was at hand, silent I stood with teeth shut close, I watch'd,
I stood very near you old man when cool and indifferent, but
    trembling with age and your unheal'd wounds, you
    mounted the scaffold;)
I would sing in my copious song your census returns of the
    States,
The tables of population and products, I would sing of your
    ships and their cargoes,
The proud black ships of Manhattan arriving, some fill'd with
    immigrants, some from the isthmus with cargoes of
    gold,
Songs thereof would I sing, to all that hitherward comes would
    I welcome give,
And you would I sing, fair stripling! welcome to you from me,
    young prince of England!
(Remember you surging Manhattan's crowds as you pass'd
    with your cortege of nobles?
There in the crowds stood I, and singled you out with attach-
    ment;)
Nor forget I to sing of the wonder, the ship as she swam up my
    bay,
Well-shaped and stately the Great Eastern swam up my bay,
    she was 600 feet long,
Her moving swiftly surrounded by myriads of small craft I
    forget not to sing;
Nor the comet that came unannounced out of the north flaring
    in heaven,

Nor the strange huge meteor-procession dazzling and clear
        shooting over our heads,
(A moment, a moment long it sail'd its balls of unearthly light
        over our heads,
Then departed, dropt in the night, and was gone;)
Of such, and fitful as they, I sing—with gleams from them
        would I gleam and patch these chants,
Your chants, O year all mottled with evil and good—year of
        forebodings!
Year of comets and meteors transient and strange—lo! even
        here one equally transient and strange!
As I flit through you hastily, soon to fall and be gone, what is
        this chant,
What am I myself but one of your meteors?

Cavalry Crossing a Ford

A line in long array where they wind betwixt green islands,
They take a serpentine course, their arms flash in the sun—
        hark to the musical clank,
Behold the silvery river, in it the splashing horses loitering
        stop to drink,
Behold the brown-faced men, each group, each person a pic-
        ture, the negligent rest on the saddles,
Some emerge on the opposite bank, others are just entering
        the ford—while,
Scarlet and blue and snowy white,
The guidon flags flutter gayly in the wind.

Vigil Strange I Kept on the Field One Night

Vigil strange I kept on the field one night;
When you my son and my comrade dropt at my side that day,
One look I but gave which your dear eyes return'd with a look
       I shall never forget,
One touch of your hand to mine O boy, reach'd up as you lay
       on the ground,
Then onward I sped in the battle, the even-contested battle,
Till late in the night reliev'd to the place at last again I made
       my way,
Found you in death so cold dear comrade, found your body son
       of responding kisses, (never again on earth respond-
       ing,)
Bared your face in the starlight, curious the scene, cool blew
       the moderate night-wind,
Long there and then in vigil I stood, dimly around me the
       battlefield spreading,
Vigil wondrous and vigil sweet there in the fragrant silent
       night,
But not a tear fell, not even a long-drawn sigh, long, long I
       gazed,
Then on the earth partially reclining sat by your side leaning
       my chin in my hands,
Passing sweet hours, immortal and mystic hours with you
       dearest comrade—not a tear, not a word,
Vigil of silence, love and death, vigil for you my son and my
       soldier,
As onward silently stars aloft, eastward new ones upward stole,
Vigil final for you brave boy, (I could not save you, swift was
       your death,
I faithfully loved you and cared for you living, I think we shall
       surely meet again,)
Till at latest lingering of the night, indeed just as the dawn
       appear'd,
My comrade I wrapt in his blanket, envelop'd well his form,

Folded the blanket well, tucking it carefully over head and
carefully under feet,
And there and then and bathed by the rising sun, my son in his
grave, in his rude-dug grave I deposited,
Ending my vigil strange with that, vigil of night and battlefield
dim,
Vigil for boy of responding kisses, (never again on earth responding,)
Vigil for comrade swiftly slain, vigil I never forget, how as
day brighten'd,
I rose from the chill ground and folded my soldier well in his
blanket,
And buried him where he fell.

Reconciliation

Word over all, beautiful as the sky,
Beautiful that war and all its deeds of carnage must in time be
utterly lost,
That the hands of the sisters Death and Night incessantly
softly wash again, and ever again, this soil'd world;
For my enemy is dead, a man divine as myself is dead,
I look where he lies white-faced and still in the coffin—I draw
near,
Bend down and touch lightly with my lips the white face in the
coffin.

125

To a Certain Civilian

Did you ask dulcet rhymes from me?
Did you seek the civilian's peaceful and languishing rhymes?
Did you find what I sang erewhile so hard to follow?
Why I was not singing erewhile for you to follow, to under-
    stand—nor am I now;
(I have been born of the same as the war was born,
The drum-corps' rattle is ever to me sweet music, I love well
    the martial dirge,
With slow wail and convulsive throb leading the officer's fu-
    neral;)
What to such as you anyhow such a poet as I? therefore leave
    my works,
And go lull yourself with what you can understand, and with
    piano-tunes,
For I lull nobody, and you will never understand me.

The Wound-Dresser

1

An old man bending I come among new faces,
Years looking backward resuming in answer to children,
Come tell us old man, as from young men and maidens that
    love me,
(Arous'd and angry, I'd thought to beat the alarum, and urge
    relentless war,
But soon my fingers fail'd me, my face droop'd and I resign'd
    myself,
To sit by the wounded and soothe them, or silently watch the
    dead;)
Years hence of these scenes, of these furious passions, these
    chances,

Of unsurpass'd heroes, (was one side so brave? the other was
      equally brave;)
Now be witness again, paint the mightiest armies of earth,
Of those armies so rapid so wondrous what saw you to tell us?
What stays with you latest and deepest? of curious panics,
Of hard-fought engagements or sieges tremendous what deep-
      est remains?

2

O maidens and young men I love and that love me,
What you ask of my days those the strangest and sudden your
      talking recalls,
Soldier alert I arrive after a long march cover'd with sweat
      and dust,
In the nick of time I come, plunge in the fight, loudly shout in
      the rush of successful charge,
Enter the captur'd works—yet lo, like a swift-running river
      they fade,
Pass and are gone they fade—I dwell not on soldiers' perils or
      soldiers' joys,
(Both I remember well—many of the hardships, few the joys,
      yet I was content.)

But in silence, in dreams' projections,
While the world of gain and appearance and mirth goes on,
So soon what is over forgotten, and waves wash the imprints
      off the sand,
With hinged knees returning I enter the doors, (while for you
      up there,
Whoever you are, follow without noise and be of strong heart.)

Bearing the bandages, water and sponge,
Straight and swift to my wounded I go,
Where they lie on the ground after the battle brought in,
Where their priceless blood reddens the grass the ground,
Or to the rows of the hospital tent, or under the roof'd hospital,
To the long rows of cots up and down each side I return,
To each and all one after another I draw near, not one do I
      miss,

An attendant follows holding a tray, he carries a refuse pail,
Soon to be fill'd with clotted rags and blood, emptied, and fill'd
　　again.

I onward go, I stop,
With hinged knees and steady hand to dress wounds,
I am firm with each, the pangs are sharp yet unavoidable,
One turns to me his appealing eyes—poor boy! I never knew
　　you,
Yet I think I could not refuse this moment to die for you, if
　　that would save you.

3

On, on I go, (open doors of time! open hospital doors!)
The crush'd head I dress, (poor crazed hand tear not the
　　bandage away,)
The neck of the cavalry-man with the bullet through and
　　through I examine,
Hard the breathing rattles, quite glazed already the eye, yet
　　life struggles hard,
(Come sweet death! be persuaded O beautiful death!
In mercy come quickly.)

A Sight in Camp in the Daybreak Gray and Dim

A sight in camp in the daybreak gray and dim,
As from my tent I emerge so early sleepless,
As slow I walk in the cool fresh air the path near by the hospital
tent,
Three forms I see on stretchers lying, brought out there un-
tended lying,
Over each the blanket spread, ample brownish woolen blanket,
Gray and heavy blanket, folding, covering all.

Curious I halt and silent stand,
Then with light fingers I from the face of the nearest the first
just lift the blanket;
Who are you elderly man so gaunt and grim, with well-gray'd
hair, and flesh all sunken about the eyes?
Who are you my dear comrade?

Then to the second I step—and who are you my child and
darling?
Who are you sweet boy with cheeks yet blooming?

Then to the third—a face nor child nor old, very calm, as of
beautiful yellow-white ivory;
Young man I think I know you—I think this face is the face
of the Christ himself,
Dead and divine and brother of all, and here again he lies.

When Lilacs Last in the Dooryard Bloom'd

1

When lilacs last in the dooryard bloom'd,
And the great star early droop'd in the western sky in the night,
I mourn'd, and yet shall mourn with ever-returning spring.

Ever-returning spring, trinity sure to me you bring,
Lilac blooming perennial and drooping star in the west,
And thought of him I love.

2

O powerful western fallen star!
O shades of night—O moody, tearful night!
O great star disappear'd—O the black murk that hides the
star!
O cruel hands that hold me powerless—O helpless soul of me!
O harsh surrounding cloud that will not free my soul.

3

In the dooryard fronting an old farm-house near the white-
wash'd palings,
Stands the lilac-bush tall-growing with heart-shaped leaves of
rich green,
With many a pointed blossom rising delicate, with the perfume
strong I love,
With every leaf a miracle—and from this bush in the dooryard,
With delicate-color'd blossoms and heart-shaped leaves of rich
green,
A sprig with its flower I break.

4

In the swamp in secluded recesses,
A shy and hidden bird is warbling a song.

130 Solitary the thrush,
The hermit withdrawn to himself, avoiding the settlements,
Sings by himself a song.

Song of the bleeding throat,
Death's outlet song of life, (for well dear brother I know,
If thou wast not granted to sing thou would'st surely die.)

5

Over the breast of the spring, the land, amid cities,
Amid lanes and through old woods, where lately the violets
    peep'd from the ground, spotting the gray debris,
Amid the grass in the fields each side of the lanes, passing the
    endless grass,
Passing the yellow-spear'd wheat, every grain from its shroud
    in the dark-brown fields uprisen,
Passing the apple-tree blows of white and pink in the orchards,
Carrying a corpse to where it shall rest in the grave,
Night and day journeys a coffin.

6

Coffin that passes through lanes and streets,
Through day and night with the great cloud darkening the
    land,
With the pomp of the inloop'd flags with the cities draped in
    black,
With the show of the States themselves as of crape-veil'd
    women standing,
With processions long and winding and the flambeaus of the
    night,
With the countless torches lit, with the silent sea of faces and
    the unbared heads,
With the waiting depot, the arriving coffin, and the sombre
    faces,
With dirges through the night, with the thousand voices rising
    strong and solemn,
With all the mournful voices of the dirges pour'd around the
    coffin,
The dim-lit churches and the shuddering organs—where amid
    these you journey,
With the tolling tolling bells' perpetual clang,

Here, coffin that slowly passes,
I give you my sprig of lilac.

7

(Nor for you, for one alone,
Blossoms and branches green to coffins all I bring,
For fresh as the morning, thus would I chant a song for you O
     sane and sacred death.

All over bouquets of roses,
O death, I cover you over with roses and early lilies,
But mostly and now the lilac that blooms the first,
Copious I break, I break the sprigs from the bushes,
With loaded arms I come, pouring for you,
For you and the coffins all of you O death.)

8

O western orb sailing the heaven,
Now I know what you must have meant as a month since I
     walk'd,
As I walk'd in silence the transparent shadowy night,
As I saw you had something to tell as you bent to me night
     after night,
As you droop'd from the sky low down as if to my side, (while
     the other stars all look'd on,)
As we wander'd together the solemn night, (for something I
     know not what kept me from sleep,)
As the night advanced, and I saw on the rim of the west how
     full you were of woe,
As I stood on the rising ground in the breeze in the cool trans-
     parent night,
As I watch'd where you pass'd and was lost in the netherward
     black of the night,
As my soul in its trouble dissatisfied sank, as where you sad
     orb,

Concluded, dropt in the night, and was gone.

Sing on there in the swamp,
O singer bashful and tender, I hear your notes, I hear your call,
I hear, I come presently, I understand you,
But a moment I linger, for the lustrous star has detain'd me,
The star my departing comrade holds and detains me.

O how shall I warble myself for the dead one there I loved?
And how shall I deck my song for the large sweet soul that has
   gone?
And what shall my perfume be for the grave of him I love?

Sea-winds blown from east and west,
Blown from the Eastern sea and blown from the Western sea,
   till there on the prairies meeting,
These and with these and the breath of my chant,
I'll perfume the grave of him I love.

11

O what shall I hang on the chamber walls?
And what shall the pictures be that I hang on the walls,
To adorn the burial-house of him I love?

Pictures of growing spring and farms and homes,
With the Fourth-month eve at sundown, and the gray smoke
   lucid and bright,
With floods of the yellow gold of the gorgeous, indolent, sinking sun, burning, expanding the air,
With the fresh sweet herbage under foot, and the pale green
   leaves of the trees prolific,
In the distance the flowing glaze, the breast of the river, with
   a wind-dapple here and there,
With ranging hills on the banks, with many a line against the
   sky, and shadows,
And the city at hand with dwellings so dense, and stacks of
   chimneys,

And all the scenes of life and the workshops, and the workmen
    homeward returning.

12

Lo, body and soul—this land,
My own Manhattan with spires, and the sparkling and hurrying
    tides, and the ships,
The varied and ample land, the South and the North in the
    light, Ohio's shores and flashing Missouri,
And ever the far-spreading prairies cover'd with grass and corn.

Lo, the most excellent sun so calm and haughty,
The violet and purple morn with just-felt breezes,
The gentle soft-born measureless light,
The miracle spreading bathing all, the fulfill'd noon,
The coming eve delicious, the welcome night and the stars,
Over my cities shining all, enveloping man and land.

13

Sing on, sing on you gray-brown bird,
Sing from the swamps, the recesses, pour your chant from the
    bushes,
Limitless out of the dusk, out of the cedars and pines.

Sing on dearest brother, warble your reedy song,
Loud human song, with voice of uttermost woe.

O liquid and free and tender!
O wild and loose to my soul—O wondrous singer!
You only I hear—yet the star holds me, (but will soon depart,)
Yet the lilac with mastering odor holds me.

14

Now while I sat in the day and look'd forth,
In the close of the day with its light and the fields of spring,
    and the farmers preparing their crops,
In the large unconscious scenery of my land with its lakes and
    forests,

In the heavenly aerial beauty, (after the perturb'd winds and
　　the storms,)
Under the arching heavens of the afternoon swift passing, and
　　the voices of children and women,
The many-moving sea-tides, and I saw the ships how they
　　sail'd,
And the summer approaching with richness, and the fields all
　　busy with labor,
And the infinite separate houses, how they all went on, each
　　with its meals and minutia of daily usages,
And the streets how their throbbings throbb'd, and the cities
　　pent—lo, then and there,
Falling upon them all and among them all, enveloping me with
　　the rest,
Appear'd the cloud, appear'd the long black trail,
And I knew death, its thought, and the sacred knowledge of
　　death.

Then with the knowledge of death as walking one side of me,
And the thought of death close-walking the other side of me,
And I in the middle as with companions, and as holding the
　　hands of companions,
I fled forth to the hiding receiving night that talks not,
Down to the shores of the water, the path by the swamp in the
　　dimness,
To the solemn shadowy cedars and ghostly pines so still.

And the singer so shy to the rest receiv'd me,
The gray-brown bird I know receiv'd us comrades three,
And he sang the carol of death, and a verse for him I love.

From deep secluded recesses,
From the fragrant cedars and the ghostly pines so still,
Came the carol of the bird.

And the charm of the carol rapt me,

As I held as if by their hands my comrades in the night,
And the voice of my spirit tallied the song of the bird.

Come lovely and soothing death,
Undulate round the world, serenely arriving, arriving,
In the day, in the night, to all, to each,
Sooner or later delicate death.

Prais'd be the fathomless universe,
For life and joy, and for objects and knowledge curious,
And for love, sweet love—but praise! praise! praise!
For the sure-enwinding arms of cool-enfolding death.

Dark mother always gliding near with soft feet,
Have none chanted for thee a chant of fullest welcome?
Then I chant it for thee, I glorify thee above all,
I bring thee a song that when thou must indeed come, come
    unfalteringly.

Approach strong deliveress,
When it is so, when thou hast taken them I joyously sing the
    dead,
Lost in the loving floating ocean of thee,
Laved in the flood of thy bliss O death.

From me to thee glad serenades,
Dances for thee I propose saluting thee, adornments and feast-
    ings for thee,
And the sights of the open landscape and the high-spread sky
    are fitting,
And life and the fields, and the huge and thoughtful night.

The night in silence under many a star,
The ocean shore and the husky whispering wave whose voice
    I know,
And the soul turning to thee O vast and well-veil'd death,
And the body gratefully nestling close to thee.

Over the tree-tops I float thee a song,
Over the rising and sinking waves, over the myriad fields and
    the prairies wide,

Over the dense-pack'd cities all and the teeming wharves and
    ways,
I float this carol with joy, with joy to thee O death.

15

To the tally of my soul,
Loud and strong kept up the gray-brown bird,
With pure deliberate notes spreading filling the night.

Loud in the pines and cedars dim,
Clear in the freshness moist and the swamp-perfume,
And I with my comrades there in the night.

While my sight that was bound in my eyes unclosed,
As to long panoramas of visions.

And I saw askant the armies,
I saw as in noiseless dreams hundreds of battle-flags,
Borne through the smoke of the battles and pierc'd with mis-
    siles I saw them,
And carried hither and yon through the smoke, and torn and
    bloody,
And at last but a few shreds left on the staffs, (and all in
    silence,)
And the staffs all splinter'd and broken.

I saw battle-corpses, myriads of them,
And the white skeletons of young men, I saw them,
I saw the debris and debris of all the slain soldiers of the war,
But I saw they were not as was thought,
They themselves were fully at rest, they suffer'd not,
The living remain'd and suffer'd, the mother suffer'd,
And the wife and the child and the musing comrade suffer'd,
And the armies that remain'd suffer'd.

16

Passing the visions, passing the night,
Passing, unloosing the hold of my comrades' hands,

Passing the song of the hermit bird and the tallying song of my soul,

Victorious song, death's outlet song, yet varying ever-altering song,

As low and wailing, yet clear the notes, rising and falling, flooding the night,

Sadly sinking and fainting, as warning and warning, and yet again bursting with joy,

Covering the earth and filling the spread of the heaven,

As that powerful psalm in the night I heard from recesses,

Passing, I leave thee lilac with heart-shaped leaves,

I leave thee there in the dooryard, blooming, returning with spring.

I cease from my song for thee,

From my gaze on thee in the west, fronting the west, communing with thee,

O comrade lustrous with silver face in the night.

Yet each to keep and all, retrievements out of the night,

The song, the wondrous chant of the gray-brown bird,

And the tallying chant, the echo arous'd in my soul,

With the lustrous and drooping star with the countenance full of woe,

With the holders holding my hand nearing the call of the bird,

Comrades mine and I in the midst, and their memory ever to keep, for the dead I loved so well,

For the sweetest, wisest soul of all my days and lands—and this for his dear sake,

Lilac and star and bird twined with the chant of my soul,

There in the fragrant pines and the cedars dusk and dim.

O Captain! My Captain!

O Captain! my Captain! our fearful trip is done,
The ship has weather'd every rack, the prize we sought is won,
The port is near, the bells I hear, the people all exulting,
While follow eyes the steady keel, the vessel grim and daring;
       But O heart! heart! heart!
          O the bleeding drops of red,
             Where on the deck my Captain lies,
               Fallen cold and dead.

O Captain! my Captain! rise up and hear the bells;
Rise up—for you the flag is flung—for you the bugle trills,
For you bouquets and ribbon'd wreaths—for you the shores
      acrowding,
For you they call, the swaying mass, their eager faces turning;
       Here Captain! dear father!
          The arm beneath your head!
             It is some dream that on the deck,
               You've fallen cold and dead.

My Captain does not answer, his lips are pale and still,
My father does not feel my arm, he has no pulse nor will,
The ship is anchor'd safe and sound, its voyage closed and
      done,
From fearful trip the victor ship comes in with object won;
       Exult O shores, and ring O bells!
        But I with mournful tread,
          Walk the deck my Captain lies,
             Fallen cold and dead.

COME,
SWEET
DEATH

Whispers of Heavenly Death

Whispers of heavenly death murmur'd I hear,
Labial gossip of night, sibilant chorals,
Footsteps gently ascending, mystical breezes wafted soft and
    low,
Ripples of unseen rivers, tides of a current flowing, forever
    flowing,
(Or is it the plashing of tears? the measureless waters of human
    tears?)

I see, just see skyward, great cloud-masses,
Mournfully slowly they roll, silently swelling and mixing,
With at times a half-dimm'd, sadden'd far-off star,
Appearing and disappearing.

(Some parturition rather, some solemn immortal birth;
On the frontiers to eyes impenetrable,
Some soul is passing over.)

Of Him I Love Day and Night

Of him I love day and night I dream'd I heard he was dead,
And I dream'd I went where they had buried him I love, but
 he was not in that place,
And I dream'd I wander'd searching among burial-places to
 find him,
And I found that every place was a burial-place;
The houses full of life were equally full of death, (this house is
 now,)
The streets, the shipping, the places of amusement, the Chi-
 cago, Boston, Philadelphia, the Mannahatta, were as
 full of the dead as of the living,
And fuller, O vastly fuller of the dead than of the living;
And what I dream'd I will henceforth tell to every person and
 age,
And I stand henceforth bound to what I dream'd,
And now I am willing to disregard burial-places and dispense
 with them,
And if the memorials of the dead were put up indifferently
 everywhere, even in the room where I eat or sleep, I
 should be satisfied,
And if the corpse of any one I love, or if my own corpse, be
 duly render'd to powder and pour'd in the sea, I shall
 be satisfied,
Or if it be distributed to the winds I shall be satisfied.

Darest Thou Now O Soul

Darest thou now O soul,
Walk out with me toward the unknown region,
Where neither ground is for the feet nor any path to follow?

No map there, nor guide,
Nor voice sounding, nor touch of human hand,
Nor face with blooming flesh, nor lips, nor eyes, are in that
land.

I know it not O soul,
Nor dost thou, all is a blank before us,
All waits undream'd of in that region, that inaccessible land.

Till when the ties loosen,
All but the ties eternal, Time and Space,
Nor darkness, gravitation, sense, nor any bounds bounding us.

Then we burst forth, we float,
In Time and Space O soul, prepared for them,
Equal, equipt at last, (O joy! O fruit of all!) them to fulfil O
soul.

An Old Man's Thought of School

(For the Inauguration of a Public School,
Camden, New Jersey, 1874)

An old man's thought of school,
An old man gathering youthful memories and blooms that
      youth itself cannot.

Now only do I know you,
O fair auroral skies—O morning dew upon the grass!
And these I see, these sparkling eyes,
These stores of mystic meaning, these young lives,
Building, equipping like a fleet of ships, immortal ships,
Soon to sail out over the measureless seas,
On the soul's voyage.

Only a lot of boys and girls?
Only the tiresome spelling, writing, ciphering classes?
Only a public school?

Ah more, infinitely more;
(As George Fox rais'd his warning cry, "Is it this pile of brick
      and mortar, these dead floors, windows, rails, you call
      the church?
Why this is not the church at all—the church is living, ever
      living souls.")

And you America,
Cast you the real reckoning for your present?
The lights and shadows of your future, good or evil?
To girlhood, boyhood look, the teacher and the school.

A Noiseless Patient Spider

A noiseless patient spider,
I mark'd where on a little promontory it stood isolated,
Mark'd how to explore the vacant vast surrounding,
It launch'd forth filament, filament, filament, out of itself,
Ever unreeling them, ever tirelessly speeding them.

And you O my soul where you stand,
Surrounded, detached, in measureless oceans of space,
Ceaselessly musing, venturing, throwing, seeking the spheres to
    connect them,
Till the bridge you will need be form'd, till the ductile anchor
    hold,
Till the gossamer thread you fling catch somewhere, O my
    soul.

To One Shortly to Die

From all the rest I single out you, having a message for you,
You are to die—let others tell you what they please, I cannot
   prevaricate,
I am exact and merciless, but I love you—there is no escape
   for you.

Softly I lay my right hand upon you, you just feel it,
I do not argue, I bend my head close and half envelop it,
I sit quietly by, I remain faithful,
I am more than nurse, more than parent or neighbor,
I absolve you from all except yourself spiritual bodily, that is
   eternal, you yourself will surely escape,
The corpse you will leave will be but excrementitious.

The sun bursts through in unlooked-for directions,
Strong thoughts fill you and confidence, you smile,
You forget you are sick, as I forget you are sick,
You do not see the medicines, you do not mind the weeping
   friends, I am with you,
I exclude others from you, there is nothing to be commiserated,
I do not commiserate, I congratulate you.

The Last Invocation

At the last, tenderly,
From the walls of the powerful fortress'd house,
From the clasp of the knitted locks, from the keep of the well-
  closed doors,
Let me be wafted.

Let me glide noiselessly forth;
With the key of softness unlock the locks—with a whisper,
Set ope the doors O soul.

Tenderly—be not impatient,
(Strong is your hold O mortal flesh,
Strong is your hold O love.)

A Clear Midnight

This is thy hour O Soul, thy free flight into the wordless,
Away from books, away from art, the day erased, the lesson
  done,
Thee fully forth emerging, silent, gazing, pondering the themes
  thou lovest best,
Night, sleep, death and the stars.

As the Time Draws Nigh

As the time draws nigh glooming a cloud,
A dread beyond of I know not what darkens me.

I shall go forth,
I shall traverse the States awhile, but I cannot tell whither or
   how long,
Perhaps soon some day or night while I am singing my voice
   will suddenly cease.

O book, O chants! must all then amount to but this?
Must we barely arrive at this beginning of us?—and yet it is
   enough, O soul;
O soul, we have positively appear'd—that is enough.

These Carols

These carols sung to cheer my passage through the world I see,
For completion I dedicate to the Invisible World.

Song at Sunset

Splendor of ended day floating and filling me,
Hour prophetic, hour resuming the past,
Inflating my throat, you divine average,
You earth and life till the last ray gleams I sing.

Open mouth of my soul uttering gladness,
Eyes of my soul seeing perfection,
Natural life of me faithfully praising things,
Corroborating forever the triumph of things.

Illustrious every one!
Illustrious what we name space, sphere of unnumber'd spirits,
Illustrious the mystery of motion in all beings, even the tiniest
      insect,
Illustrious the attribute of speech, the senses, the body,
Illustrious the passing light—illustrious the pale reflection on
      the new moon in the western sky,
Illustrious whatever I see or hear or touch, to the last.

Good in all,
In the satisfaction and aplomb of animals,
In the annual return of the seasons,
In the hilarity of youth,
In the strength and flush of manhood,
In the grandeur and exquisiteness of old age,
In the superb vistas of death.

Wonderful to depart!
Wonderful to be here!
The heart, to jet the all-alike and innocent blood!
To breathe the air, how delicious!
To speak—to walk—to seize something by the hand!
To prepare for sleep, for bed, to look on my rose-color'd flesh!
To be conscious of my body, so satisfied, so large!
To be this incredible God I am!

To have gone forth among other Gods, these men and women I
love.

Wonderful how I celebrate you and myself!
How my thoughts play subtly at the spectacles around!
How the clouds pass silently overhead!
How the earth darts on and on! and how the sun, moon, stars,
dart on and on!
How the water sports and sings! (surely it is alive!)
How the trees rise and stand up, with strong trunks, with
branches and leaves!
(Surely there is something more in each of the trees, some
living soul.)

O amazement of things—even the least particle!
O spirituality of things!
O strain musical flowing through ages and continents, now
reaching me and America!
I take your strong chords, intersperse them, and cheerfully pass
them forward.

I too carol the sun, usher'd or at noon, or as now, setting,
I too throb to the brain and beauty of the earth and of all the
growths of the earth,
I too have felt the resistless call of myself.

As I steam'd down the Mississippi,
As I wander'd over the prairies,
As I have lived, as I have look'd through my windows my eyes,
As I went forth in the morning, as I beheld the light breaking in
the east,
As I bathed on the beach of the Eastern Sea, and again on the
beach of Western Sea,
As I roam'd the streets of inland Chicago, whatever streets I
have roam'd,
Or cities or silent woods, or even amid the sights of war,
Wherever I have been I have charged myself with content-
ment and triumph.

I sing to the last equalities modern or old,
I sing the endless finalés of things,
I say Nature continues, glory continues,
I praise with electric voice,
For I do not see one imperfection in the universe,
And I do not see one cause or result lamentable at last in the
    universe.

O setting sun! though the time has come,
I still warble under you, if none else does, unmitigated adora-
    tion.

Now Finalé to the Shore

Now finalé to the shore,
Now land and life finalé and farewell,
Now Voyager depart, (much, much for thee is yet in store,)
Often enough hast thou adventur'd o'er the seas,
Cautiously cruising, studying the charts,
Duly again to port and hawser's tie returning;
But now obey thy cherish'd secret wish,
Embrace thy friends, leave all in order,
To port and hawser's tie no more returning,
Depart upon thy endless cruise old Sailor.

So Long!

To conclude, I announce what comes after me.

I remember I said before my leaves sprang at all,
I would raise my voice jocund and strong with reference to
consummations.

When America does what was promis'd,
When through these States walk a hundred millions of superb
persons,
When the rest part away for superb persons and contribute to
them,
When breeds of the most perfect mothers denote America,
Then to me and mine our due fruition.

I have press'd through in my own right,
I have sung the body and the soul, war and peace have I sung,
and the songs of life and death,
And the songs of birth, and shown that there are many births.

I have offer'd my style to every one, I have journey'd with con-
fident step;
While my pleasure is yet at the full I whisper *So long!*
And take the young woman's hand and the young man's hand
for the last time.

I announce natural persons to arise,
I announce justice triumphant,
I announce uncompromising liberty and equality,
I announce the justification of candor and the justification of
pride.

I announce that the identity of these States is a single identity
only,

I announce the Union more and more compact, indissoluble,
I announce splendors and majesties to make all the previous
politics of the earth insignificant.
I announce adhesiveness, I say it shall be limitless, unloosen'd,
I say you shall yet find the friend you were looking for.

I announce a man or woman coming, perhaps you are the one,
(So long!)
I announce the great individual, fluid as Nature, chaste, affec-
tionate, compassionate, fully arm'd.

I announce a life that shall be copious, vehement, spiritual,
bold,
I announce an end that shall lightly and joyfully meet its trans-
lation.

I announce myriads of youths, beautiful, gigantic, sweet-
blooded,
I announce a race of splendid and savage old men.

O thicker and faster—(So long!)
O crowding too close upon me,
I foresee too much, it means more than I thought,
It appears to me I am dying.

Hasten throat and sound your last,
Salute me—salute the days once more. Peal the old cry once
more.

Screaming electric, the atmosphere using,
At random glancing, each as I notice absorbing,
Swiftly on, but a little while alighting,
Curious envelop'd messages delivering,
Sparkles hot, seed ethereal down in the dirt dropping,
154 Myself unknowing, my commission obeying, to question it
never daring,
To ages and ages yet the growth of the seed leaving,

To troops out of the war arising, they the task I have set pro-
mulging,
To women certain whispers of myself bequeathing, their affection me more clearly explaining,
To young men my problems offering—no dallier I—I the
muscle of their brains crying,
So I pass, a little time vocal, visible, contrary,
Afterward a melodious echo, passionately bent for, (death
making me really undying,)
The best of me then when no longer visible, for toward that I
have been incessantly preparing.

What is there more, that I lag and pause and crouch extended
with unshut mouth?
Is there a single final farewell?

My songs cease, I abandon them,
From behind the screen where I hid I advance personally
solely to you.

Camerado, this is no book,
Who touches this touches a man,
(Is it night? are we here together alone?)
It is I you hold and who holds you,
I spring from the pages into your arms—decease calls me
forth.

O how your fingers drowse me,
Your breath falls around me like dew, your pulse lulls the
tympans of my ears,
I feel immerged from head to foot;
Delicious, enough.

Enough O deed impromptu and secret,
Enough O gliding present—enough O summ'd-up past.

Dear friend whoever you are take this kiss,
I give it especially to you, do not forget me,

I feel like one who has done work for the day to retire awhile,
I receive now again of my many translations, from my avataras
    ascending, while others doubtless await me,
An unknown sphere more real than I dream'd, more direct,
    darts awakening rays about me, *So long!*
Remember my words, I may again return,
I love you, I depart from materials,
I am as one disembodied, triumphant, dead.

After the Supper and Talk

After the supper and talk—after the day is done,
As a friend from friends his final withdrawal prolonging,
Good-bye and Good-bye with emotional lips repeating,
(So hard for his hand to release those hands—no more will
    they meet,
No more for communion of sorrow and joy, of old and young,
A far-stretching journey awaits him, to return no more,)
Shunning, postponing severance—seeking to ward off the last
    word ever so little,
E'en at the exit-door turning—charges superfluous calling back
    —e'en as he descends the steps,
Something to eke out a minute additional—shadows of night-
    fall deepening,
Farewells, messages lessening—dimmer the forthgoer's visage
    and form,
156 Soon to be lost for aye in the darkness—loth, O so loth to de-
    part!
Garrulous to the very last.

Good-bye My Fancy!

Good-bye my Fancy!
Farewell dear mate, dear love!
I'm going away, I know not where,
Or to what fortune, or whether I may ever see you again,
So Good-bye my Fancy.

Now for my last—let me look back a moment;
The slower fainter ticking of the clock is in me,
Exit, nightfall, and soon the heart-thud stopping.

Long have we lived, joy'd, caress'd together;
Delightful!—now separation—Good-bye my Fancy.

Yet let me not be too hasty,
Long indeed have we lived, slept, filter'd, become really
         blended into one;
Then if we die together, (yes, we'll remain one,)
If we go anywhere we'll go together to meet what happens,
May-be we'll be better off and blither, and learn something,
May-be it is yourself now really ushering me to the true songs,
         (who knows?)
May-be it is you the mortal knob really undoing, turning—so
         now finally,
Good-bye—and hail! my Fancy.

Poets to Come

Poets to come! orators, singers, musicians to come!
Not to-day is to justify me and answer what I am for,
But you, a new brood, native, athletic, continental, greater than
      before known,
Arouse! For you must justify me.

I myself but write one or two indicative words for the future,
I but advance a moment only to wheel and hurry back in the
      darkness.

I am a man who, sauntering along without fully stopping, turns
      a casual look upon you and then averts his face,
Leaving it to you to prove and define it,
Expecting the main things from you.

A Whitman Reading List

1. *Leaves of Grass.* With an Introduction by Gay Wilson Allen. New York, New American Library of World Literature, 1960.

>   A paperback which includes the final text of 1892 with a biocritical introduction.

2. *The Portable Walt Whitman.* Selected and edited by Mark Van Doren. New York, The Viking Press, 1945.

>   Available in both hardbound and paperback editions, this selection includes Whitman's best poetry and prose, and the preface to the first edition of *Leaves of Grass.*

3. *Walt Whitman Handbook.* By Gay Wilson Allen. New York, Farrar, Straus and Company, Inc., 1946.

>   A useful summary of the biographical and critical works on Whitman in many languages.

4. *Walt Whitman, Builder for America.* By Babette Deutsch. Illustrated by Raphael Busoni. New York, Julian Messner, Inc., 1941.

>   An excellent biography for young readers, with a selection of poems and bibliography.

5. *Walt Whitman and the Springs of Courage.* By Haniel Long. Santa Fe, New Mexico, Writers' Editions, Inc., 1938.

>   This is a book which deeply understands and illuminates the humane genius of the poet.

Index
of Titles

163

Index of First Lines

About the Compiler

Lawrence Clark Powell, Dean of the School of Library Service at the University of California, Los Angeles, is not only one of the foremost librarians in the country, but a scholar, a gifted writer, and a lecturer. As a testimony to his lifelong work with books, the American Library Association presented him with the first Clarence Day award in 1960 for the encouragement of a love of books and reading.

Dean Powell was born in Washington, D.C., but his family moved shorty thereafter to California where he attended public schools and was graduated from Occidental College. His graduate study was undertaken in France, and he received his Ph.D. from the University of Dijon. He is active in many educational and library associations and he has lectured extensively in the United States, Europe, and Asia.

He is the author of numerous books and has frequently written articles for professional and literary journals and magazines.

About the Artists

Clare Romano Ross and John Ross were trained at the Cooper Union School of Art and studied at the Ecole des Beaux Arts, Fontainebleau, France, and at the Istituto Statale, Florence, Italy. The Rosses were awarded Tiffany Fellowships for printmaking and lived in Italy for a year under a Fulbright grant for woodcuts. They are represented in museums throughout the United States and their work is in the permanent collection of the Metropolitan Museum of Art.

Mr. and Mrs. Ross live and work in New Jersey, a short distance from New York City where they teach. Mr. Ross is president of the Society of American Graphic Artists.